Healthcare Allocation: an ethical framework for public policy

Healthcare Allocation: an ethical framework for public policy

edited by

Anthony Fisher OP

and

Luke Gormally

The Linacre Centre

London

Published on behalf of
The Catholic Bishops' Joint Bioethics Committee
by
The Linacre Centre for Healthcare Ethics
60 Grove End Road, London, NW8 9NH

First published 2001

British Library Cataloguing in Publication Data
A catalogue record for this book is available from the British Library

ISBN 0 906561 19 1

Typeset by Academic + Technical, Bristol
Printed and bound by The Bath Press

Contents

Foreword   xi

Preface   xiii

Introduction: Crisis in the NHS   xv

Part I   Preliminaries   1

1   Clarifying some central terms of the debate   3
   1.1   Introduction   3
   1.2   What is health?   4
   1.3   What is healthcare?   5
   1.4   Healthcare resources and healthcare systems   6
   1.5   Healthcare allocation   7

2   Background to the current crisis in healthcare allocation   9

3   Some standard responses to scarcity   13
   3.1   'Spend more'   13
   3.2   'Be more efficient'   14
   3.3   'Distribute better'   15

4   Ethical issues in the allocation debate and the content of this Report   17
   4.1   Themes in contemporary reflection on healthcare allocation   17
   4.2   What principles ought to govern the allocation of healthcare?   18
   4.3   The content of this Report   21

Part II Healthcare Allocation: Unsystematic Approaches and the Contemporary Search for Principled Solutions   **23**

5 Unsystematic approaches: allocating resources without planning   **25**
5.1   Introduction   25
5.2   'Ad hocery'   26
5.3   Leaving it to the market   27
     5.3.1   'The free market'   27
     5.3.2   The rights of healthworkers in a free market   28
     5.3.3   The rights of taxpayers in a free market   30
     5.3.4   The rights of would-be patients in a free market   32
     5.3.5   The rôle of the state in a free market   32
     5.3.6   Is a free-market in healthcare possible and just?   33
5.4   Conclusion   35

6 The contemporary search for principled solutions (1): What basis for principles?   **37**
6.1   Introduction   37
6.2   Neutral principles?   38
6.3   Consensus principles?   40
6.4   Arbitrary principles?   41

7 The contemporary search for principled solutions (2): Liberal-welfarist approaches   **45**
7.1   'Health for all' – the traditional NHS approach   45
7.2   *Liberty* above all: the contemporary idolization of autonomy   47
7.3   *Equality*: equitable access to healthcare so as to ensure roughly equal life opportunities   49
7.4   *Fraternity*: should special provision be made for the healthcare of the disadvantaged?   51
7.5   Advantages and disadvantages of the liberal-welfarist approach   52

8 The contemporary search for principled solutions (3): Utilitarian-economic approaches   **55**
8.1   Introduction   55
8.2   Applied utilitarianism (A): QALYs   56
8.3   Applied utilitarianism (B): The Oregon Scheme   57

8.4	Which benefits, which losses?	58
8.5	Problems with counting benefits and losses	61
8.6	Justice and other values	64
8.7	Beyond simple justice: mercy and the Good Samaritan	67
8.8	Conclusion	68
	Conclusion to Part II	71

Part III   A Framework of Moral Understanding for Healthcare Allocation — **73**

9	**Towards a substantive conception of the human good**	**75**
9.1	The notion of the good(s)	76
9.2	Life and health as basic goods	76
9.3	Why needs matter	78
9.4	Moral norms	79
9.5	Moral virtues	80
9.6	Conclusion	81

10	**Persons and their needs**	**83**
10.1	Human beings are embodied	83
10.2	Human beings have needs and healthcare is one	84
10.3	Not everything that goes by the name of healthcare satisfies a need	86
10.4	Needs are the basis of *prima facie* but not absolute duties	88
10.5	Individuals should attend to their own needs	89

11	**The nature of human community and the provision of healthcare**	**91**
11.1	The need for a substantive conception of community	92
11.2	Healthcare begins at home	94
11.3	Healthcare is also a social good	95
11.4	Healthcare is a matter of distributive justice	97
11.5	Different communities will give differing degrees of priority to healthcare	98
11.6	Socio-cultural differences do not serve to call in question a right to healthcare	100
11.7	Towards a substantive conception of healthcare practice	103
	Conclusion to Part III	106

**Part IV Criteria and Considerations relevant to
Allocation Decisions**   **107**

12 Inadequate allocation criteria   **109**
  12.1 To each equally   109
  12.2 To each according to the free market   112
  12.3 To each according to their social contribution   113
  12.4 To each according to their desert or merit   114
      12.4.1 '*Women* and children first': a preference for
             those with dependants   115
      12.4.2 'Women and *children* first': a preference for the
             young   115
      12.4.3 A more general preference for younger over
             older patients   116
      12.4.4 'We shouldn't be wasting resources on those
             with severe brain damage': mental ability
             and minimum quality of life as a basis for
             rationing   119
      12.4.5 'Smokers and drinkers shouldn't expect public
             health': reward for personal responsibility   123

13 To each according to his/her need   **127**
      Conclusion to Chapters 12 and 13   132

14 Other considerations in healthcare allocation   **133**
  14.1 Introduction   134
  14.2 Competing social goals   134
  14.3 Basic rights must be respected   136
  14.4 Directly homicidal or harmful healthcare allocations   136
  14.5 Indirectly homicidal and harmful healthcare allocations   137
  14.6 Punitive healthcare allocations   138
  14.7 Prejudiced healthcare allocations   139
  14.8 Those at risk: the frail elderly, the handicapped, the
      mentally ill, the poor   139

Part V Catholic Social Teaching   **143**

15 Catholic social teaching and the allocation of healthcare   **145**
  15.1 Introduction   145
  15.2 The dignity of the human person and the right to
      live and flourish   147

15.3 The right to healthcare   151
15.4 The option for the poor and sick   152
15.5 The responsibility of the community to respond to
      healthcare needs   153
15.6 The limits to autonomy in property ownership and
      healthcare   155
15.7 The principle of subsidiarity   157
15.8 The model of the Good Samaritan   158
15.9 Conclusion   160

Part VI Conclusion   **163**

16 Implications for public policy   **165**
16.1 How much should be spent on healthcare?   165
16.2 Should a right to healthcare be recognized?   167
16.3 Other legislative action   173
16.4 How should the total sum allocated to healthcare be
      divided?   174
16.5 What mix of government and private?   175
16.6 Who should keep the gate?   177
16.7 The need for public debate on these matters   180

17 Summary and Conclusions   **183**

Endnotes   **193**

Index   **229**

Foreword

It is evident in all contemporary societies that at least some of the demand for healthcare cannot be met, if only because demand invariably outstrips available resources. Hence, there are problems of allocating resources. In these circumstances, the provision of healthcare should at least ensure both that patients – particularly the more vulnerable among them – should not suffer injustices, and that the principles of sound medical and nursing care should not be undermined.

It became clear to the Catholic Bishops' Joint Bioethics Committee some years ago that standard approaches to healthcare allocation policy among economists, policy analysts and ethicists not only failed to identify some of the fundamental moral issues at stake but would also lead to injustices to patients and damage to the character of the healthcare professions. The moral frameworks – whether explicit or implicit – informing debates about allocation policy have been seriously defective, and a number of decisions in the courts have served to reinforce the influence of these defects.

The Committee decided to invite a small Working Group, under the chairmanship of Mr Luke Gormally, Director of The Linacre Centre for Healthcare Ethics, to prepare a substantial document which would show what was defective in prevailing approaches to healthcare allocation and propose a more adequate moral framework for allocation policy. As Luke Gormally explains in his Preface, for a variety of reasons the preparation of the resultant Report has been protracted. I am confident, however, that it remains even more relevant today than when it was first commissioned.

On behalf of The Catholic Bishops' Joint Bioethics Committee, I would like to thank Luke Gormally and his colleagues in the Working Group for their labours in preparing this Report; a particular debt of gratitude is owing to the Very Reverend Professor Anthony Fisher OP. I would also like to thank those members of The Catholic

Bishops' Joint Bioethics Committee who collaborated with Luke in the later stages of preparing the text.

You do not have to be a Catholic to understand and appreciate this Report: it offers a reasoned case for the wisdom it seeks to commend. That wisdom has undoubtedly matured, however, as a result of the Catholic Church's long-standing involvement in the provision of healthcare. The oldest provider of healthcare in the world, she still remains the largest provider of healthcare. There is a wealth of experience as well as reflection behind this Report. My hope is that it will serve to bring some badly needed moral wisdom to the discussion of healthcare allocation policy, especially in Great Britain and Ireland.

Thomas J Cardinal Winning

Chairman, The Catholic Bishops' Joint Bioethics Committee.

Preface

As Cardinal Winning's Foreword indicates, the following Report was commissioned to provide both an ethical critique of prevailing approaches to healthcare allocation and a more adequate ethical framework for public policy.

The original Working Group that accepted this commission had the following membership: Dr Harry Burns (Director of Public Health, Greater Glasgow Health Board*); Fr Anthony Fisher OP (in the later stages of our deliberations, Lecturer in Ethics, Australian Catholic University, Melbourne); Professor Michael Horan (Professor of Geriatric Medicine, University of Manchester); Mr Patrick Kinder CBE (Chief Executive, Eastern Area Health Board, Northern Ireland); Fr David Morland OSB (philosopher and theologian, Ampleforth Abbey, York); and the present writer. We began our deliberations a decade ago. The most important contributor to our work was Fr Anthony Fisher OP, whom we were fortunate to recruit to the Group, since at the time he was doing research at Oxford directly relevant to our interests. He wrote the first two drafts of our Report, which have remained the basis of all subsequent work on it. The work of the Group was disrupted, however, by two circumstances: the return of Fr Fisher to Australia in 1995 to take up a number of demanding appointments there, and illnesses the present writer had in 1995 and 1996 which, given a number of other pressing commitments, made resumption of work on the Report difficult. When I eventually found it possible to resume work on the Report, discussion of its form and content to a large extent shifted from the original Working Group to plenary meetings of the Catholic Bishops' Joint Bioethics Committee. In the latter stages of the work of editing and redrafting

---

* The positions indicated in the text are in most cases those held at the time the Working Group was convened.

I was particularly assisted by criticisms and suggestions from a group of members of the Bishops' Committee deputed to review final drafts: Bishop Christopher Budd, Bishop Donal Murray, Dr John McLean, Dr Anna Murphy, and Professor Peter Millard. Professor Millard was especially generous in the assistance he provided at this stage.

Dr Harry Burns, from the original Working Group, supplied detailed criticisms of the penultimate draft, and Fr Anthony Fisher OP, in a working session in London in September 2000, was able to share in the task of shaping the final draft, which in large part retains his original work. At various stages, preparation of the Report has benefited from the advice of Professor John Finnis FBA and of Dr John Keown, who helped with the drafting of parts of Chapter 16.

Given the complex and protracted nature of the work involved in producing this Report, it would be unreasonable to expect every contributor to that work to be answerable for every sentence in the Report. The text is, however, published with the approval of The Catholic Bishops' Joint Bioethics Committee as a contribution to public policy debate, which articulates the moral requirements an allocation policy should meet not only to avoid injustice to patients and the subversion of the healthcare professions, but also to ensure that healthcare in our society uncompromisingly serves the common good.

Luke Gormally

Introduction

'Crisis' in the National Health Service

This Report is concerned to establish an adequate ethical framework for the allocation of healthcare, with particular reference to the UK. The need to do so has arisen largely because of what are perceived to be failures in the National Health Service which raise issues of resource allocation. So the Report begins by introducing the issues in relation to what is sometimes spoken of as a 'crisis' in the National Health Service.

The National Health Service (NHS) is today said to be in 'crisis.' Underlying the rhetoric of such claims there are some serious issues which challenge Christians and all people of good will. Whereas some countries are too poor to provide even the most basic standards of healthcare for their populations, and others, though prosperous, do not even try, the UK has long been notable for its attempt to provide healthcare for all its citizens. In the past few years, however, there have been an increasing number of complaints about equity and comprehensiveness of access. There is a disturbing frequency to cases in which the media report failures of care or other failures in the health service and, more often than not, the underlying issue raised concerns the proper allocation of finite resources. The same basic issue, in a variety of manifestations, recurrently arises in other countries.

In recent years there has been a growing volume of publications, including Government Reports (The Netherlands, New Zealand, Sweden), addressing the problems of resource allocation in health care. Some of these publications propose solutions based on an inadequate understanding of the purpose of the health care system (such as: maximising 'health gain'), others propose solutions which are unsatisfactory because they fail to take account of all the principles which should govern the framing of allocation policy. It is common, for example, to claim that a policy is satisfactory if it satisfies the demands of equity and efficiency. But equity takes care of only some of the requirements of justice, and may fail to do even that in the absence of a true understanding of who it is who should be treated equitably.

It is not our conviction that there is a uniquely correct solution for the UK, still less for all similar economies, to the problems of health-care resource allocation. Nor is it our conviction that there is a uniquely correct approach to finding solutions. So this Report does not seek to propound any one approach, still less any one solution, to resolving the problems of healthcare resource allocation in the UK.

It is, however, clear to us that much current thinking (and hence practice) in regard to resource allocation is intellectually and morally impoverished. The present Report seeks above all to contribute to remedying this situation. First, by identifying the inadequacies of some of the characteristic approaches to resource allocation; secondly, by explaining the relevance of a number of considerations that are often overlooked in formulating resource allocation policy. We hope that our effort to direct attention to these considerations will serve to inform public policy and so the general understanding of the common good.

Part I

Preliminaries

1

Clarifying some central terms of the debate

This chapter begins by clarifying the idea of health as a necessary preliminary to defining what healthcare is. It goes on to consider what are included in the resources and systems which serve healthcare. The chapter concludes by distinguishing the general idea of 'allocation' from the more specific idea of 'rationing', which may be explicit or implicit. The levels at which rationing takes place within the overall system of the NHS are distinguished.

1.1 Introduction

If we are to discuss the *allocation* of healthcare we need to clarify the notion of 'healthcare'. We cannot be satisfied with the view that healthcare just is what 'healthcarers' do. A decision to count as healthcare whatever may be claimed to be healthcare overlooks the need to distinguish between genuine and spurious claims of that kind. If we deny the need to make such a distinction we might as well abandon the aspiration to establish a reasonable basis for decisions about allocating resources to healthcare. How can one defend allocating resources to a practice simply because people conventionally regarded as healthcarers carry it out? There is some recognition of the pertinence of this question, as is evident from the limited debates about the justifiability of funding treatments such as *in vitro* fertilization. But a normative conception of what is to count as healthcare will, as we shall see, call into question more practices than certain forms of infertility treatment.

3

1.2 What is health?

It seems clear that the notion of 'healthcare' needs to be elucidated through clarifying the notion of 'health' and the related notion of 'ill-health'. So we begin by offering some clarification of the idea of 'health'.

There are various understandings of health and ill-health advanced in our society. The World Health Organization defined health as 'a state of complete physical, mental, and social well-being, and not merely the absence of disease or infirmity.'[1] While this definition reflects what might be thought to be an admirable concern for the whole person, it amounts to equating health with happiness. Happiness (or the integral fulfilment of persons) is, as we shall see in Chapter 9, properly the object of all human activity. While health is, generally speaking,[2] a crucial element and precondition of human well-being or flourishing, human flourishing requires many other ingredient elements: moral and intellectual dispositions and a range of skills. And it is clear that not all evils experienced by human beings are manifestations of ill-health.[3] There is a particular danger in contemporary societies, impressed by the achievements of medicine, of 'medicalizing' the whole of human experience.

Too broad an understanding of health can result in vacuity: every dimension of human flourishing can be called 'health' and every kind of failure to flourish 'ill-health', so that a great variety of human activities are then deemed to be in some sense 'healthcare'. This can lead to an inappropriate analysis of situations and to the application of inappropriate 'solutions'. It can also lead to misdirection of the efforts of health professionals and misuse of medical resources. The health professions have developed with a particular history, mores, and goals internal to their practice, which leave their members ill-suited and ill-resourced to perform other roles and functions; to expect healthworkers to be omnicompetent about all that is required for human well-being is unreasonable and destroys the coherence of healthcare as a distinctive undertaking.

Another understanding of health, commonly proposed by psychiatrists and social theorists, is 'the ability to function well in society'. On the face of it health does seem to be 'relative' to people's own temperaments (their 'pain tolerance thresholds', or whether or not they are of sanguine disposition), their goals (paraplegia is likely to affect the life of a footballer rather more drastically than the life of a physicist), their physical environment (asthma and hay-fever depend upon surrounding air conditions), and their social situation (until European settlement, dyslexia was no handicap among Australian Aborigines because they did not have writing). Yet all these factors only show the relativity (and even this, not absolutely) of the *significance* of health and sickness to people; they do not show the non-existence of somatic disabilities or of breakdown or impairment of functional capacities. Of course people can adjust in a better or worse fashion to their situations, and communities can assist or hinder that adjustment: but there remains something proper to the physical reality of that person which may require a response from others, and society's response may well tell us more about what is wrong with that society than about what is wrong with the individual. Were health judged purely in terms of social adjustment, all social non-conformity would or could be characterized as disease and would be 'treated' by 'medical' means such as quarantine, psychoactive drugs and psychological techniques: the fact that we deplore these very interpretations and practices by some tyrannical régimes reflects the fact that there is more to health than social adjustment.

In the present Report we accept the classical biomedical or organic understanding of health. Health, on this view, is the well-ordered organic functioning of the body, such as well serves a human being's survival and flourishing. In the human species this will include the biological prerequisites for its 'animal' activities, such as nutrition, sentience, motility and reproduction, and for its specifically 'human' activities, such as emotional responsiveness, understanding, judgement, choice, and the acquisition of these abilities, in association with the progressive mastery of language. An emphasis on bodily or biological health is not intended to deny the importance of other aspects of the human person (psychological, moral, or spiritual) or to deny the complex interdependence of these various dimensions of the person. Both in terms of cause and effect organic health will commonly be related to other dimensions of well-being.

1.3 What is healthcare?

Healthcare is the 'healing' arts (underpinned by science) of medicine and nursing and all that allied clinical activity which seeks the promotion, maintenance and restoration of health or the alleviation of distressing symptoms of ill-health. Traditionally it has first and foremost focused on disease and injury (which will have objective clinical signs), as well as their associated psychological or emotional effects (illness, pain and suffering) and their effects on activity and social interaction (disability and handicap).

Not everything doctors and nurses do contributes to the restoration or maintenance of health and the alleviation of symptoms. Sometimes this is because what they do is futile or even harmful. At other times it is because some of the things healthworkers do have other ends in view: reducing non-medical suffering or inconvenience (by, for example, regulating fertility); providing non-medical consumer wants (cosmetic surgery, selecting characteristics of children, sex-change operations); 'health enhancement' (through the administration of drugs or by operations which aim not at correcting or alleviating defects of structure or function but at securing achievements beyond the otherwise healthy natural endowments of an individual); maximizing income, avoiding litigation or achieving research or career goals; or collaborating in social objectives such as eugenics. These activities are not true 'healthcare'; whatever merits they may be thought to have, their justification (if any) lies elsewhere.

Health is served by personal activities other than healthcare – such as eating and taking exercise – as well as by other human activities affecting the quality of housing, water, sewerage and the environment. Healthcare, on the other hand, is *clinical* care, a service generally provided by people with particular ends, skills and strategies, who belong to the health professions – although, of course, others might also supply the kind of care these professionals provide. In chapters 9 to 11 we will explore at greater length the importance of healthcare being seen as more than just the application of a technical skill in accordance with the idiosyncratic attitudes and wishes of doctor and patient. The complex interrelationship between health and other aspects of human well-being also means that 'holistic' care for real people will require more than simple 'body mechanics': good healthcare will reflect an awareness of the complexity of the persons it serves and will be co-ordinated with other kinds of care (with some of which it inevitably overlaps) such as social services, with other efforts to improve the physical and social environment, with counselling and chaplaincy, and so on.

1.4 Healthcare resources and healthcare systems

Healthcare resources are whatever is used in the provision of healthcare. This would include funding (NHS budgets provided from consolidated revenues, private insurance payments, charity funds, out-of-pocket payments), infrastructure (hospitals, beds, technical equipment ranging from simple scalpels to MRI scanners), labour (the number, kind, time and energies of healthworkers, the posts in certain specialties, the opportunities for training and research), and items used (swabs, drugs, blood, organs for transplant). Particular procedures or therapies usually involve some combination of these.

The health system as a whole is a complex of resources, institutions, policies, practices, persons and actions which provides healthcare in a particular community. Commonly in Britain we use the term to refer to the NHS, but there are of course various healthcare activities outside the purview of the government funded and regulated system. Nor need the word 'system' here imply a simple or unified, 'systematic' or planned provision, or a clear and identifiable agent or group of agents directing the activity: a free market in healthcare or a mixed system involving some combination of public-and-free, public-but-for-a-charge, joint-public-and-private, private-but-regulated and private-and-unregulated services are all kinds of 'system'. (Since the 1991 reforms, the NHS has itself become a 'mixed system'.) Any health system necessarily overlaps with other social systems such as those providing welfare, housing, education, sewerage and water.

1.5 Healthcare allocation

The notion of 'allocation' may be used of any distribution of resources whether or not the distribution takes place as the result of a policy or of a decision made with precisely that end in view. By contrast the notions of 'rationing' and 'prioritization' imply decision-making which is more or less systematic in character.

The system which characterises rationing decisions may be implicit or explicit. When it is *implicit* it is there to be found in the pattern of decisions taken, but this pattern is not publicly acknowledged and justified. The general practitioner in his role as 'gatekeeper', allowing or barring access to specialist or other types of care, has been a principal agent of largely unacknowledged rationing in the history of the National Health Service. But there has been a certain pattern to such rationing exhibited, for example, in the widespread disinclination to allow elderly patients access to expensive medical treatments.

When rationing is *explicit* the bases for rationing decisions are publicly acknowledged and justifications for them may be offered.

In relation to the NHS it is helpful to distinguish the different levels at which rationing decisions take place.

The first and highest level is around the Cabinet table, where decisions are made about how much money to allocate to healthcare after assessing the competing claims on public finances of education, housing, social security, defence, the administration of justice, and so on.

The second level is the one at which the total budget allocation at the disposal of a health authority is divided among different sectors or care groups. What should go to the elderly? What should go to antenatal care? What should go to those suffering from renal failure? The UK Government declines to recommend priority setting principles, and has confined itself to setting targets for reducing the incidence of certain conditions (such as coronary disease and cancer) and for reducing waiting lists. Local health authorities are responsible for their own priority setting.

The third level of rationing is the level at which resources are allocated to types of organizational provision (e.g. hospital or community care) or to types of treatment (e.g. renal transplantation for those suffering from renal failure). The Government declines to exclude from NHS provision any particular service and has only very rarely sought to exclude a particular treatment. In theory local health authorities are free to do so; in practice a number of health authorities who have exercised this freedom have mostly found themselves obliged to reverse their decisions.

The fourth level of rationing is the one at which individual clinicians make decisions about how to use the resources available to them: i.e. decisions about *which* patients they are in a position to treat and about *how much* care or treatment to give to individual patients.

2

Background to the current crisis in healthcare allocation

The current crisis in the NHS has been caused by a number of factors: the exponential rate at which new diagnostic techniques and treatments (often in themselves expensive) have developed since its establishment and the consequent growth in people's expectations of healthcare; increased lifespan and the consequent increased burden of chronic diseases; the increased incidence of a number of conditions such as cancers and sexually transmitted diseases; and the 'medicalization' of conditions which previously did not come within the purview of medicine. The increased costs of healthcare mean that there cannot be universal access to everything people would *count* as healthcare. Rationing has always been a feature of the NHS but has become a much more explicit concern with the organizational changes of the past decade.

Until this century, though much treatment was attempted, very little was actually achieved in healthcare: it had little effect on health. The majority of effective treatments which were known were commonly 'home remedies'. Nonetheless, those with the means to do so consulted medical practitioners for their additional but limited knowledge and skill. In the medieval period, institutions such as monastic hostels and pharmacies, and subsequently asylums and poor houses funded by public subscriptions, and some other charitable institutions, helped to fill the gap where the poor were concerned. But the advance of medical technology and the associated specialization and institutionalization have made it more difficult to accommodate and afford 'all that medicine can provide'.

9

In response to this difficulty and to the perceived inequities in the older national health insurance plan (enacted under Lloyd George in 1911), and in keeping with the post-war sense of solidarity and welfarism, the National Health Service was introduced in Britain and Northern Ireland in 1948.[1] At that time the government took direct control of UK health insurance funds, clinics and hospitals, sought to control the distribution of GPs, and accepted responsibility for funding most primary and secondary healthcare.

From its inception the ideal of the NHS has been to provide universal access to comprehensive cradle-to-grave healthcare, irrespective of any factor other than healthcare need.[2] This ideal has been repeatedly articulated by all major political parties, and remains to this day the ostensible goal of the health service. The measure to which the ideal has been achieved during the past fifty years is indeed remarkable, and present difficulties should not blind us to the fact that the NHS has been in many respects one of the most impressive institutional achievements of post-WWII society in the UK.

The optimistic assumption of the authors of the NHS was that universal access to healthcare would so improve the health of the nation that expenditure would, in time, actually diminish. The incidence of certain diseases was in fact reduced; some were even eradicated. But the potential savings were eclipsed by new demand. Within a year of the inception of the health service the government placed caps on its budget and introduced co-payments for dentistry, drugs and spectacles. Health spending has risen from 3.5% of GDP in the first full year of the NHS to almost 7%,[3] and it is still growing, if at a slower rate than previously. The most obvious causes of rising costs have been the exponential rate at which new diagnostic techniques and new treatments have been developed since the Second World War together with greatly increased staff salaries. New and better treatments are naturally greeted with enthusiasm by both doctors and patients. The Hippocratic ethic of doing everything possible to help the patient has seemed to require, precisely because of the considerable advances in healthcare, a 'hi-tech', limitlessly expensive medicine. Special factors which have contributed to increased demand for certain types of healthcare have included the extended life-span of many chronic care patients[4] and recent 'epidemics' of particular conditions such as coronary disease, various cancers, Alzheimer's Disease, sexually transmitted diseases, AIDS, infertility, asthma and allergies.

But at least as significant as technological developments have been changes in social expectations. Government funding and private insurance mean much more can now be afforded, and is expected, by ordinary people. Legal developments have contributed to a significant increase in 'defensive' medicine.[5] Individuals are also increasingly aware of health matters and of medical possibilities, due in part to education and advertising. The 'medicalization' of a great deal of human experience has meant that conditions (such as depression or childbirth) which might once have been dealt with in other ways (by priests, wise elders, midwives, friends) are now commonly treated medically. We are also probably less willing to put up with pain and disability than were our ancestors: people often expect fairly immediate relief from discomforts, and look to technology and service-providers to satisfy this expectation.

There is a tendency, therefore, in modern Western societies to demand ever-increasing provision of healthcare and to regard every possible medical treatment as a right incompatible with cost-limiting and rationing measures. Healthcare now makes a major contribution to health and welfare, but at a constantly increasing cost despite some economies of scale. The pressure on resources, as well as the range of factors affecting distribution, make it more and more difficult to ensure universal access to the whole range of beneficial therapies.

It should be recognized, however, that Britain's almost universal and fairly comprehensive health service has at least up till now been provided at remarkably low cost. Because of lower wages among healthworkers, lower healthcare expectations in the community generally, budget limitations imposed by government and health authorities, and a sense among healthworkers that they are informal custodians of a finite public resource, the UK health service has been provided at a cost significantly below that of most comparable countries.[6] This has, however, meant that some 'hi-tech' interventions are less common here. Haemodialysis, for instance, is notoriously less available in Britain than elsewhere, especially for the elderly.[7]

Furthermore, despite good 'value for money' and increased spending in real terms, the health system no longer keeps pace with demand, especially with respect to conditions that are not life-threatening. Apart from simple non-provision, a first-come-first-served system of queuing has long been in place in the NHS, with 'queue-hopping' allowed in more urgent cases. This is the principal form of overt rationing in Britain, especially of specialist healthcare; less explicit factors have been professional traditions, medical fashion and reputation, 'who you know', and (for those who want private treatment) ability to pay.

In the last decade of the 20th century the NHS underwent radical changes in its management structures which have had important implications for the allocation of healthcare resources. In 1991 a split was introduced in the NHS between healthcare purchasers (district health authorities and GP fundholders) who buy healthcare on behalf of patients and healthcare providers (usually hospitals) who sell it; this was supposed to generate greater competition and efficiency, more local and flexible decision making, greater accountability and increased patient choice. Previously district health authorities had planned and administered the provision of most hospital and community services to meet the needs of those in their district; GPs provided primary care to patients and made referrals to hospital and community services. In the 1990s, however, it came to be the case that self-governing hospital trusts (accountable to the Secretary of State for Health through the eight regional offices of the National Health Service Executive) provided hospital services: they tendered for contracts and sold their services to the purchasing authorities; if they spent 'over target' they would not be reimbursed, so they had a very strong incentive to keep to their contracts. The budgets of purchasing authorities were strictly confined and pressures brought to bear to provide more services for less. The arrangement, which obtained under the Conservative Administration, whereby GP fundholders held their own budgets and could purchase specified hospital, outpatient and community health services, has been transformed by the present Labour Administration in favour of Plurality-based primary care groups that now have the responsibility for purchasing such services.[8]

It is clear, then, that many people, at different levels of the NHS, are confronted with the necessity of making resource allocation decisions. It is important that those decisions should take account of the full range of ethical considerations relevant to them.

3

Some standard responses to scarcity

This chapter considers the inadequacy of exclusive reliance on one or other of two responses to the lack of healthcare resources: that what is required is simply additional expenditure or that what is required is simply greater efficiency in the use of available resources. Neither response makes avoidable the need to ration.

3.1 'Spend more'

Emergencies such as war, natural disasters, or major accidents focus attention on the problems of allocating healthcare resources; so do the inevitable shortages of certain new or expensive treatments, or of organs for transplant. Some treatments eventually become commonplace due to professional practice, falling unit costs, or political decisions to fund, while others remain underfunded or under-provided. Some therapies are widely available, while others are available only to the privileged few. But if we were to seek to give everyone whatever is medically appropriate it would cost rather more than we presently allow for healthcare.

One obvious response to this problem would be to increase the resources allotted. Calls for rationing and for greater efficiency can distract attention from the question whether the financial resources given to the NHS should be increased. As already noted, Britain spends significantly less on healthcare per person than comparable nations and, from the 1970s onwards, has had the longest waiting lists for newer technologies in the developed world. Plublic expenditure on the NHS has never kept pace with Health Department estimates of needs. Thus some argue that the problem is not one of limited resources, but of misallocation of social resources to less important things. Economic insecurity, an already high tax-burden, and an ideological shift away from welfarism, may have resulted in what should be judged to be insufficient allocation of resources to healthcare.

Should more resources be allocated, in one way or another, to healthcare? In raising this question we also need to recognise that a growing number of economists and policymakers are convinced that the current rate of growth in healthcare expenditures is not sustainable. Throughout the world, governments and insurers are trying to rein back the acceleration of healthcare costs, though not without considerable resistance. In the UK around a tenth of all public spending already goes to this end – more than double the amount spent by government on education, transport, or law and order. Healthcare seems to have an appetite so voracious that it could consume available resources at the expense of all other worthy social goals and programmes. So it seems clear that the injunction to 'spend more' cannot be our only response in the face of increasing demand, even if *some* increase in spending is indicated.

3.2 'Be more efficient'

Another response to the problem of healthcare allocation is to seek to use existing or budgeted healthcare resources more efficiently. In the 1970s and 1980s the official NHS strategy for dealing with resource shortages was 'rationalising' or 'efficiency savings'. The underlying idea was that growing demand could be met by increased efficiency. Providers were required to make efficiency savings of around 1.5% to 2.5% per annum.

Undoubtedly there is much that could be done to reduce inefficient management and work practices, the application of inappropriate treatments, therapies of high expense and of little or no benefit, and so on. There is evidence that the 1990s NHS reforms yielded some efficiency improvements, a greater awareness of costs among all those involved in the health system, and increased utilisation of the useful discipline of clinical audit. Various services were privatised and savings made in other ways. But it was commonly observed about these 1991 reforms that they led to excessive spending on management at the expense of service to patients and to 'efficiency improvements' only by reducing activity, distributing resources away from the poor, the sick and the elderly, and increasingly transferring costs to the individual, family and local community. The present Labour Government is committed to reducing management costs in favour of patient care.

However important efficiency may be, greater efficiency is hardly a sufficient response to the contemporary challenge of healthcare provision. No amount of efficiency will increase the number of doctors and nurses who may be needed; nor will it abolish the possibility of sudden increases in demand due to disasters or epidemics of one kind or another; nor will it slow the inexorable rise in demand we have already noted; nor will it make up for plain under-resourcing. As a Dutch government committee concluded in 1992, increased efficiency 'can probably delay the need to make choices in healthcare, but cannot ultimately prevent it'.[1]

3.3 'Distribute better'

A third response to the healthcare resources problem is to face up to the fact that not everyone can have every possible treatment, and to seek to ensure that the unavoidable allocation of resources occurs in the best way possible. Rationing *is* inevitable because of the finitude of human life, technology, institutions, human and natural resources, and because of the 'opportunity costs' (alternatives forgone) with every choice. It has always occurred in the form of queues, delays, dilution of services, disincentives, diversion to other providers, and plain non-provision. Healthworkers have always made judgments about where to put their time and energies, who would benefit more from a scarce resource, and so on. Politicians and health service managers have likewise made choices about where money should be spent and, by implication, where not. Major institutions have arisen in particular places and not in others. The choice, then, is not between rationing healthcare or not, but between allocating in an unreflective, unarticulated way, and rationing in a more explicit, systematic and principled way, while allowing for some unavoidable flexibility and 'untidiness'. In either case, individual decisions, policies and systems, and their overall effect on the members of the community, should be assessed by reference to moral principles.

Throughout the world people are gradually facing up to these realities. Government committees in several European countries, the

United States, the US state of Oregon, New Zealand and Australia have all made recommendations in this area. In 1991 the European Ministers of Health met in Noordwijk to consider the problems of making choices in healthcare. In the UK there have always been caps on secondary healthcare and since the 1970s some efforts to redistribute services geographically according to objective needs.[2] More recently health ministers and authorities, while uneasy about confessing to 'rationing' in the health system, have begun to speak openly about the need to 'prioritize' healthcare.

While one of the aims of the introduction of the purchaser-provider split in the NHS was that health authorities should determine their resource allocation in the light of local needs rather than inherited patterns of services, very few health authorities have excluded any specific services from NHS provision so far, and these have only excluded certain cosmetic and infertility treatments from the free list. This amounts to symbolic 'rationing at the edges' only.[3] But more thoroughgoing prioritization and rationing seems unavoidable. Some health economists and managers propose the use of utilitarian allocational devices such as 'QALYs' (see 8.2 below); some health authorities, following the Oregon model (see 8.3 below), are asking local people about their health priorities; and there is undoubtedly a growing consciousness of healthcare costs and the need to distribute resources more justly and efficiently.

Each of the standard broad responses to the reality of scarcity in the provision of healthcare will raise, if given practical application, questions about whether the resultant distribution of resources is morally defensible. So we turn to a preliminary consideration of the kind of ethical issues which feature in discussions of resource allocation.

4

Ethical issues in the allocation debate and the content of this Report

This chapter briefly identifies some common themes in contemporary reflection on healthcare allocation, offers a broad characterization of the idea of justice which will be at the centre of the Report, and outlines the structure of the remainder of the Report.

4.1 Themes in contemporary reflection on healthcare allocation

Traditional medical ethics focused almost single-mindedly on the doctor-patient relationship, paying no systematic attention to the issue of rationing raised by limited resources. The broader social context of the doctor-patient relationship was not in all respects ignored. Reflection on the ethics of quarantine in case of public health risk, on the public nature of the healthcare 'vocation', and especially regarding professional duties to the poor, reflected some concern for 'the common good'.

In the last few years there has been a proliferation of professional literature and political statements about healthcare allocation. Five themes recur in much of that writing. First, it is widely asserted that healthcare is a right – though the basis, scope and limits of this right are rarely explained. Secondly, costs are said to be escalating beyond the capacity of health systems and national budgets to bear. Thirdly, it is claimed that privatization and a shift towards the free market will help to achieve greater healthcare value for the pound. Fourthly, it is proposed that the careful application of utilitarian quality of life and economic cost-benefit techniques could establish a more rational system of healthcare allocation. And finally, health systems are charged with being riddled with inequities, such as: under-spending on healthcare (relative to demand or to supply in comparable countries) or overspending on healthcare (relative to other social goods); a disproportionate focus on (observable) disease rather than (experienced) illness, on sickness rather than health, on cure rather than prevention, on 'hi-tech', institutional care rather than simpler remedies and institutions, on traditional or fashionable kinds of healthcare rather than research, complementary and unglamorous kinds of healthcare, and on short- and medium-term rather than chronic and long-term care; overspending on those patients, therapies, disciplines or healthworkers which have particular political, ideolo-gical or emotional clout; unjust discrimination on the basis of factors such as institutional tradition, profitability, professional repu-tation, race, religion, gender, regional and social location, age, handicap or articulateness; and a lack of appropriate discrimination on the basis of youth, disadvantage, personal responsibility for illness, or economic or quality of life criteria.

Sometimes questions are raised about the evidence for these charges; but equally important are questions about the ethical basis on which particular distributions are to be judged unjust. Without a coherent set of moral principles allegations may be mere question-begging, prejudice or interest-peddling. It will emerge that we do think that there are significant misallocations of resources in the NHS and that there is a real risk that these will worsen in the future. But this conten-tion must at least in part rest on canons of criticism offered by reflec-tion on justice; without such norms there is no solid basis for challenging misallocations.

4.2 What principles ought to govern the allocation of healthcare?

We come, therefore, to the central concern of the present report: what principles ought to govern the allocation of healthcare in the UK? By focusing on healthcare justice in the contemporary UK, we shall eschew certain related questions of undoubted importance which deserve separate treatments, such as international justice, intergenerational justice (except regarding an age criterion), and duties towards (non-human) animals. *Similarly, we shall focus upon the principles upon which NHS resources should be allocated, rather than the appropriate processes by which policy should be formulated and implemented, who should bear the burden of provision and according to what measure, what particular medical therapies or institutions are most beneficial, and so on.* It will be more than enough to treat directly of the question of what principles ought to govern the allocation of healthcare within the NHS. Obviously practical approaches to resolving allocation problems will also have to take account of data, perspectives and standards drawn from medicine, policy studies, economics and politics. Fundamental here, however, will be ethics or morality: in particular, the principles of justice.

What should be said in a preliminary way about justice? This is not the place to survey the history or contemporary literature on justice. It is enough here to note a few points. First, *justice* (and its cognates) is a quality predicated of persons, choices and whole complexes of persons and choices.[1] That is why we can speak of a just man or woman, an unjust institution or community, a fair policy or strategy, an unfair situation or system.

Secondly, justice is part of *morality*. There are, of course, many different theories of morality and thus of justice. We will in general be drawing upon 'classical' or 'common' morality (about which more below) and later (chapter 15) bringing out the extent to which Catholic social and bioethical teaching to a great extent coincides with it. Together they provide us with an understanding of appropriate standards of moral evaluation. But it must be admitted that they do not identify a single 'right' approach to allocation problems. So there is some need to consider competing approaches, see what they have to say about healthcare allocation, and then assess whether these answers are adequate in terms of the requirements of sound moral reflection.

Thirdly, justice is that part of morality which concerns right relations *between persons*. It assumes some commonality of life and interests; it is a quality of character and choices, and of situations, institutions and policies created by choice which favours and fosters the common good of *communities*. Thus a systematic account of justice, on this view, is an account of what requirements we should meet in our choices if they are to favour the common good.[2]

Fourthly, justice is traditionally defined as 'giving to others *their due*' or respecting people's rights and entitlements, and discriminating

19

between persons only on the basis of a 'morally relevant difference'.[3] But 'due' and 'rights' in this context should not be conceived too narrowly, as they are by those who view them as referring only to obligations under contract or promise, to non-interference rights, and to appropriate respect for the laws of the land, due process and the like. Justice certainly does concern these matters, but it should also be conceived more broadly, as concerned with what counts as *upright dealing* with others *in all respects*. Thus, rather than being viewed as entirely distinct from qualities such as equity and charity, which are seen in turn as optional adjuncts to justice, 'tempering' or 'transcending' it, we shall conceive of these adjuncts as needed in applying justice (narrowly conceived) in any real situation and as integral to good relations between persons generally (justice more broadly conceived).

Fifthly, *distributive* justice concerns the distribution of benefits (such as healthcare) and burdens to the appropriate person(s) according to appropriate criteria. In chapters 12 and 13 we shall scrutinize several considerations invoked in determining what is justice in distribution: equality, need and disadvantage; the requirement that distribution should be determined by the more or less unfettered operation of the 'free market'; social value; age; consciousness and quality of life; and personal responsibility. *Whatever we settle on as properly determining justice in distribution, it would be a mistake to think that the justice we seek in allocating resources is fully determined by such considerations. We also need to consider what other fundamental principles and basic rights might be compromised by any particular scheme for healthcare allocation.* (See chapter 14.)

Not only do people today differ, sometimes radically, from their fellows in their conceptions of justice (and in their ethical convictions more generally), but many try to hold together some incoherent amalgam of beliefs inherited from different ethical traditions. As we shall see in chapters 5 to 8, some hold that to be just one must act on the basis of those constraints which any rational and impartial person would agree should be imposed; still others, on the basis of seeking one's own ends whatever they might be and avoiding interfering with others; others, on the basis of a balance between a few established principles of medical ethics; others, by calculating, comparing and maximizing net benefits; and others again, on the basis of some more fully elaborated theory of practical reason. Such fundamental disagreements often go unacknowledged, 'disguised by a rhetoric of consensus', and discourse becomes both incoherent and adversarial.[4] *Part of the object of the present study, therefore, will be to uncover these unclarities and differences and propose a basis for dialogue and (where appropriate) reform.*

The aspiration to provide a basis for dialogue involves no assumption that all competing theories can be reconciled or that one particular theory of justice will yield a uniquely correct set of answers to the multifarious questions which arise in determining what is required if healthcare resources are to be distributed justly. Our object is a rather more humble and, we hope, achievable one: to identify the basic framework of moral principles which should govern the allocation of healthcare if it is to be just.

4.3 The content of this Report

Having noted some of the defining features of the contemporary debate about healthcare allocation, we shall proceed in the following chapters to examine a number of traditional and contemporary approaches (chapters 5 to 8), all of which have led to serious impasses. In chapters 9 to 11 we shall propose a more substantive, 'natural law' alternative which avoids these difficulties by attending to the goods of the human person and community, and the norms and virtues which follow therefrom. In seeking to articulate a coherent understanding of the requirements of justice in healthcare allocation, we hope to provide a framework by which principled resolutions to practical disagreements over the distribution of resources can be found. Any practical reliance on such a framework will however require a clear concept of what particular criteria are appropriate to the distribution of healthcare (chapters 12 and 13) and what other basic principles and rights need to be recognised if distributional arrangements are to be acceptable (chapter 14). On this basis we can identify certain injustices or tendencies to injustice in the present system and draw some conclusions for public policy in the UK (chapter 16).

The underlying assumptions and orientations of this report are Christian and draw in particular on the Christian natural law tradition, especially in bioethics, and that body of teaching known as 'Catholic social teaching', as these have evolved over many centuries of healthcare practice and moral reflection on political economy and society. That tradition, it should be noted, characteristically appeals to *reason* and to experience. We believe that Catholic thinking in this area has a unique contribution to make partly because of the long association of the Church with healthcare (it has been and continues to be the world's biggest healthcare provider), its centuries of accumulated experience and wisdom in dealing with healthcare dilemmas, and the particular gifts of inspiration and reason which it brings to bear on social problems more generally. We shall analyse the specifically Catholic contribution to our topic in chapter 15. We believe that what we say here is generally compatible with the best of our 'common morality' articulated in such places as the Bible and the Koran, the Hippocratic Oath, the common law, international human rights documents, and the teachings of many thinkers both secular and religious. *We have chosen points of departure, a method of argumentation and a language shared by many outside our faith tradition in the hope that much of our argumentation and our conclusions will appeal to people of good will of all faiths and none, and will invite constructive dialogue on what is, because of its radical implications for so many, potentially the weightiest bioethical issue confronting us.*

Part II

Healthcare Allocation: Unsystematic Approaches and the Contemporary Search for Principled Solutions

5

Unsystematic approaches: allocating resources without planning

In this chapter we consider relatively unplanned allocation of healthcare resources. This may be an historically entrenched phenomenon resulting from particular balances of power (as in much of the history of the NHS) or an ideological goal (as in advocacy of a 'free market' in healthcare). The fundamental criticism to be made of unplanned allocations is that they fall far short of what people may reasonably expect in the way of justice in the allocation of healthcare. 'Free market' opposition to those expectations is both theoretically and practically defective. It is theoretically defective in that it is founded on an inadequate understanding of what is needed for human flourishing and what is therefore required for the common good. It is practically defective in that it offers no prospect of meeting those needs and requirements.

5.1 Introduction

In this and the following three chapters we shall examine some long-standing and contemporary approaches to healthcare allocation. We cannot pretend to survey the whole range of approaches which have been or could be taken: rather, we have selected a few representative and highly influential ones for presentation and examination. In this chapter we shall consider two approaches to distributing healthcare which avoid systematic planning: '*ad hocery*' and leaving allocation to 'the market'.

5.2 'Ad hocery'

The history of the medical profession and of the NHS, as well as the complex of factors affecting demand and supply noted previously, have meant that healthcare allocation in the UK throughout much of the history of the NHS has been a rather *ad hoc* process. Commonly it occurred by default, the unplanned result of a variety of other decisions and goals, such as the choice to 'do things as we always have', or the choice to 'leave it to the doctors to decide'. Total budgets and the distribution of health resources were in consequence the product of a complicated and often mysterious variety of forces and values: the vagaries of demand and projected demand; long-standing professional practice and more recent fashions; medium- and long-term political and bureaucratic planning and 'knee-jerk' responses to particular issues; the interests and views of the medical colleges, associations and journals, and of hospital department heads and other professional leaders; the custom of queuing and of queue-jumping for 'medical necessity'; the operation of the 'free' market; decisions of private healthcare providers and insurers; regional and demographic factors; and so on. Despite increased awareness of healthcare allocation issues in recent years, and increased attention to it among healthcare managers, there is still no well-established trend towards a more coherent distribution of healthcare.

Lack of a formal approach to distribution does have what may be thought to be advantages: it can allow considerable scope to the autonomy of the professions and their members, which may have the effect of encouraging professional responsibility, creativity and initiative; it can give practitioners room to respond to complex and unprovided-for circumstances, and allow for a variety of perspectives and policies to contend for ascendancy or to co-exist. The disadvantages, however, follow from the fact that so much is left up to 'happenstance': who happens to have power or influence at a particular time, where one happens to live, who one knows, and so on. Those who distribute are left to determine their own standards, whether they are chosen consciously or unconsciously, rationally or arbitrarily, selfinterestedly or altruistically. Prejudices and smallness of vision can easily creep in, decisions can be arbitrary and unpredictable, and some, who might otherwise have enjoyed access to care, will not. One commentator has pointed to some of the other risks:

> *ad hoc* selection is unfair. It has no built-in consistency, and 'Who shall decide?' completely eclipses the matter of 'How

shall they decide?' The question of power replaces the concern for justice. The receiving of treatment hinges upon who the patients are and how persuasively they can present their case for being treated. As a result, mistrust and tension build between physician and patient, and the value society places upon human life and the equal worth of persons is eroded.[1]

We will argue in Parts III and IV that health planners and workers are required by justice to distribute resources not primarily to satisfy their own preferences and to further their own projects, but rather to meet the reasonable needs of others. But first we should consider the position of principled opposition to planned distribution of healthcare – the view that distribution should be left to the operations of the 'free market'.

5.3 Leaving it to the market

5.3.1 'The free market'

Until World War II healthcare was commonly allocated upon the basis of the doctor's willingness to provide and the patient's willingness to pay – although there were always significant exceptions to this. Reforms introduced into the NHS in the 1980s and 1990s represented an ideological and practical shift back to a more market-oriented health system, and because this remains a major tendency in thinking about the NHS we shall give this approach extended attention in this chapter. Several other European countries and some Commonwealth ones have also been moving towards new mixes of government, semi-government and private provision, with greater reliance upon 'internal' and external markets, the principle of 'user-pays', and private health insurance. *Prima facie* at least, these trends are broadly consistent with certain 'libertarian' political philosophies and economic theories, have their advocates in the literature of bioethics, and have shaped the language in which healthcare provision is discussed ('health-care consumers', 'customers' or 'clients', 'service-providers', 'the healthcare market', 'demand and supply', 'throughput', etc.).

The 'free market', it must be recognized, is an idealized relationship between persons, production, distribution and exchange: probably no absolutely free market has ever existed, certainly not in healthcare. Its advocates, however, begin with the now broadly accepted principle that everyone has rights which guarantee that his or her person and property will not be non-consensually interfered with; justice, for these theorists, is principally or entirely about respect for such rights. Individuals should be left to use their natural endowments and just holdings to make whatever deals they wish; they should devote their wealth, income and energy to whatever ends they choose; they may decide to be charitable towards the unfortunate, or they may not; either way it is no business of the state or anyone else to force their hand.

On the face of it such a position would seem to deny that there is any right to healthcare or any societal responsibility to provide it, and to recommend the freemarket as the only just system of allocation: it is up to people individually to choose what healthcover or services they wish to spend their resources on; and up to health professionals to decide how, when and where they want to work, as well as for whom, with whom, and for how much. We should not, however, assume that all forms of advocacy of a 'free market' carry these alleged implications. Some advocates may be prepared to recognise other entitlements.

5.3.2 The rights of healthworkers in a free market

On the pure free-market view, healthworkers are no more required to provide care according to need or some other criterion proposed by moralists or the state than are barbers. Health professionals own their own skills and labour and may choose as they please how they exercise those skills, subject of course to any undertakings they have made to others. Their relationship to their patients is one of service-provider to customer or client: they must keep their promises and not harm their customers (except, perhaps, with the customer's consent). On this basis proponents of the free market recognize that accepting people onto one's list or providing care to them over several years may establish quasi-contractual relationships which properly restrict the physician's later choices; likewise admitting a person into an institution may amount to an undertaking of some sort. Difficulties arise for these theorists, however, where offers or undertakings are *implied by a social context*: if, for instance, it is understood by all in a community that doctors will give emergency assistance to anyone brought to them, it could be viewed as a term of an (unspoken) agreement made by the physician with the community upon entering into professional training or practice.

Contracts (and possibly conventions) aside, however, a free-market theorist would support an 'unconstrained' approach which leaves healthcare distribution up to the choice of healthcare providers and thus the free market. Providers would decide for themselves what rationing standards (if any) to apply in their own practices: profit maximization through treating those who pay most; personal satisfaction through treating those one prefers; or some more altruistic standard such as preference for those in greatest need. This would be entirely a matter for individual service-providers to decide for themselves: any attempt by the government or any other moral 'busy-body' to force distribution of healthcare into some particular ideal pattern would require 'enslavement' of healthworkers. Underneath this rhetoric there is an important point being made here: most healthcare is not a natural resource like an uncultivated medicinal herb; even if healthcare employs a great deal of common property, healthworkers are not livestock to be distributed according to someone else's interests or grand plan. Health professionals are people and therefore never to be viewed merely as means to other people's ends, and talk of distributing 'human resources' in healthcare can obscure this point.

But even free-marketeers recognize that there is a need to regulate and/or redistribute in situations of monopoly or oligopoly. This is for two reasons: first, because the advantages of the free market in terms of efficiency in pricing and provision of services may be compromised if one party has excessive control of the market; and secondly, because the appropriation or exploitation of a monopoly over some necessity undermines the moral foundations of ownership.[2] This could preclude a health professional, whether alone or in collusion with others (the hospital, profession etc.), withholding provision for a basic human need or extorting high rates for access to it.[3]

One must also be wary of sliding too quickly or simply from the (not unproblematical) notion of 'self-ownership' to an assertion of the right to dispose of one's talents, in what one does, as one pleases, and then from this to the right to dispose of all the fruits of those actions however one wishes. Health professionals do not merely provide 'the sweat of their brows' to their patients: they provide a particular skill. And that skill is not purely of their own creation, however crucial free will and personal motivation are in its cultivation and application. Healthworkers are educated largely at the public expense and usually in public institutions, and the knowledge they receive is a social product

29

not of their own making. What is more, without a high level of collaboration there would be no sophisticated healthcare, no acute care hospitals, drugs and so forth. Societies and their institutions provide the necessary human and material resources and support the rôles and opportunities for people to engage in this collaborative enterprise. And if most health providers do not in any straightforward way own the goods and services which they co-operate in producing and do not in general own all the means of producing them, then the use of state power to 'direct' or 'redistribute' these goods and services is not necessarily an infringement of entitlements: *it may instead be the most effective way of returning to all their due.*

Furthermore, if healthcare providers want to receive certain resources and opportunities – huge investments of tax monies in medical institutions, professional monopolies through licensing, protection by patents and other legal privileges, subsidy and high rewards for services provided – then they have to allow that the providers of those resources and opportunities will have some say in how they are used. Membership of a profession also entails certain responsibilities – a matter to which we shall return in chapter 11 (see especially 11.7). The liberal model of the self-owned, self-determining 'man against the world' presumes too naïve a view of agency, too atomistic a view of interpersonal relations, and too thin a concept of community and tradition, to apply to the everyday lives of real healthworkers. At least until now a large body of health professionals in the UK have taken a much more community-minded view of their responsibilities regarding the services they 'own' or control.

5.3.3 The rights of taxpayers in a free market

Advocates of a free health market do not exclude the possibility of very large charitable endowments sufficient to fund free hospitals of high standard for indigents and others. But on their view human dignity and need, community and the state, do not as such ground any positive obligations and entitlements; there are only negative rights and duties of non-interference. Wealth-owners and income-earners must be protected from expropriation of wealth and income to which they are entitled. Even where done by legitimate authority and for some socially beneficial cause such as healthcare, indeed even where done for the benefit of the taxpayers themselves, such non-consensual expropriation through taxation is, on this view 'theft' or 'forced labour'.[4] Such a claim is of course an overstatement to the extent that the labour is voluntary and the taxpayer has a say in the tax policy. Without being naïve about how really free workers are, especially in times of high unemployment, it remains that no one decides who must work, or for whom, or how hard, or for how long, and that those who decide to take a job do so knowing that a certain percentage of their gross income will go in taxes. In democracies, at least, they can also influence the level of those taxes and how they are spent. Furthermore, supporters of the free market themselves allow *some* taxation for (among other things) the wages of the legitimate officers of the state, restitution for non-consenting victims of decisions or failures of the state as a security guard, and certain other necessities for the functioning of a community. But they would regard taxation to finance welfare programmes, including the NHS, as an illegitimate imposition upon any non-consenting taxpayer.

This contention presumes a fairly straightforward identification of who is entitled to what. Free-market theorists generally adopt some variety of John Locke's doctrine that, subject to certain provisos, persons are entitled to: anything they appropriate which belongs to no-one else (land, raw materials, abandoned goods...); the fruits of their own efforts and of the application of their efforts to any resource which is unowned or already theirs; and those things which they obtain justly from others, by voluntary gift or exchange. But this view prompts obvious objections. In the first place, it relies upon an unsupported assertion that natural resources, until worked by someone, 'belong to nobody'; others would argue that, until privately acquired and even to some extent thereafter, they belong to everybody.[5] Secondly, on Locke's own account, acquisition from a 'state of nature' is only just if certain caveats are observed, which commonly are not.[6] Thirdly, few would claim that all they hold has, at all previous points in its history of transfer, been free of any form of injustice in its acquisition. If it were to be the case that actual property entitlements were of a 'free-market' kind that would suggest that many, indeed most, contemporary property holdings are unjust.[7] How could such injustices be calculated and repaired? Given the complexities, some have suggested that redistributive taxation and welfare payments, including healthcare, might be the simplest form of 'restitution' or 'rectification'.[8]

What is most obviously lacking in most free-market accounts of property entitlements, however, is an adequate account of the ends of private property (whether in acquisition, transfer or use) in terms of its value for the individual and the common good. We shall return to this matter in chapter 11.

5.3.4 The rights of would-be patients in a free market

For free-market theorists the only genuine rights are negative (non-interference) rights, and so there is no right to healthcare. People are free to take whatever risks they please with their own health and to invest as much or as little as they wish in maintaining and improving their health. Healthcare, on this account, is a matter of choice rather than right – at least for those who can pay.

5.3.5 The rôle of the state in a free market

Free-market theorists generally allow the state only a limited 'security guard' rôle – protecting people from non-consensual interference with their persons and property, and against theft and fraud, arbitrating in disputes, enforcing contracts, and so on; any more extensive state would, however well-intentioned, inevitably violate people's rights and dignity. Any attempt by the state to ensure access of some or all to healthcare through taxation or regulation or to ensure any particular pattern of healthcare distribution would require the state's abandonment of its proper neutrality between various views of the good life, its adoption of a particular conception, and its imposition upon persons who do not agree. Against this it might be argued that just as people are willing to surrender a certain amount of liberty to the state in order that it can guarantee law and order, so they might be presumed to be willing to pay (and to surrender certain rights) in order to be secure against catastrophic disease, a threat at least as great to their livelihood and in some ways just as violent as breaches of law and order?[9] The alternative – in which the state stands by while one section of the population lacks necessities such as basic healthcare and another section has the best of healthcare and indulges itself with extravagances – would be very socially corrosive. Even public projects justified by the direst need (e.g. public health measures in times of plague) could be obstructed by the determined non-intervention of the state or by the refusal of those with property to support the project. In chapter 11 we shall propose an alternative view of the rôle of the state as not only a protector of liberties but also a coordinator and (within the bounds of subsidiarity) a guarantor, even provider, of the requirements of the common good such as healthcare for members of the community.

5.3.6 Is a free-market in healthcare possible and just?

Some people romanticize the unregulated free market, others demonize it. The free market approach draws attention to the importance of autonomy and noninterference rights, and invites vigilance against tyrannical majoritarianism, governmental paternalism, creeping bureaucracy and unnecessary centralization. It serves to highlight the importance of people being free and encouraged to take responsibility for their own health and healthcare. It also recognizes that health services are not just unclaimed natural resources or part of some amorphous social pot: they are intimately connected with the activity of particular individuals whose various involvements must be respected and duly rewarded. Free-market elements in health systems offer other advantages too: respect for conscience and for various minority conceptions of the good; broad scope for individuals and associations to engage in charitable works such as healthcare; incentives to efficiency, initiative and responsibility; and disincentives to a 'cargo cult' mentality where people look to others or to the state to provide everything in their lives.

But fundamental problems emerge for any thoroughgoing free-market approach to healthcare allocation. Some aspects of healthcare make it a peculiar kind of good not well-suited to market distribution:

- people with great healthcare needs and/or few resources will find it difficult or impossible to get insurance or care, or to do so without prejudicing other necessary or reasonable life-goals;
- others, though not so needy, will still be subject to severe restrictions on bargaining power (we shall return to this matter below);
- the profession has monopoly power through licensing;
- physicians as agents for the patients often determine the appropriate tests and treatment: thus there is only one party on both sides of the supposed market transaction – something all the more problematical when physicians get 'kickbacks' from or own the laboratories, hospitals or other specialist services to which they refer their patients or get other distorting incentives through the insurance or government payment system;
- health authorities, hospital trusts, doctors or insurers may engage in 'cream skimming', i.e. preferring higher profit procedures or patients with low healthcare needs or risk, and leaving others 'out in the cold';

- even the freest healthcare markets have various rigidities which make them notoriously unresponsive to consumer preferences;
- supply of some medical goods cannot easily be increased and sale of some medical 'goods' is unethical (e.g. organs);
- as in all markets, but perhaps more strongly in healthcare, irrational preferences are common among both providers and consumers; and
- the market neglects preventative health strategies and research into areas unlikely to yield short-term profits since no individuals are deemed to have responsibility for public health in general or towards future generations.

For these reasons and others, the free market alone has historically been unable to deliver broadly available, cheap, good quality health-care; spending in (relatively) free-market America is galloping out of control, while the same services are provided much more cheaply and universally in less market-oriented systems such as in the UK. Furthermore, economists have long recognized that the smooth opera-tion of the (otherwise) 'free' market requires some non-market inter-ventions and the provision of 'public goods' such as law and order, security, education and so on. Healthcare, it may very well be argued, is such a good: without reliable health standards in a commu-nity, commerce and industry will be ill-effected. Thus a less-than-free market in healthcare may be a prerequisite to a fairly free market in other matters.

Even if a genuine free market in healthcare were practicable, however, would it be just? We have already called into question much of the theoretical basis of this approach: its concepts of the indi-vidual and the state, of property and services. The reliance upon the 'invisible hand' and the 'trickle down effect' of the market to ensure that most or all ('in the long run') be better off in terms of access to healthcare is unsupported in healthcare practice. Whether this lack of access and the various distributional 'distortions' are judged unjust depends, of course, upon one's understanding of justice and, as we have seen, libertarians regard as just any system which confines itself to guaranteeing people's non-interference rights. Time and again recourse is had by advocates of the market to simplistic distinctions between the unjust and the unlucky, or the just and the charitable, or political justice and moral life. They provide little reason to accept that human flourishing will best be served by a free market: their analysis of the workings of the market is too naïve and their treatment of human flourishing too cursory.

Human choices, practices and institutions as complex as healthcare are not reducible to the simple logic of the free market and presumed merit and consent. Nor is state neutrality either ideal or possible. A free-market society would discourage activities not rewarded by the market and may treat those who fail to succeed as less worthy and those who act out of benevolence as gullible.

If there are both theoretical and practical reasons to regard a free-market approach to healthcare allocation as seriously flawed, this does not mean that certain market emphases might not remain applicable and valuable. There may, for instance, be no objection in principle to differential provision or to people purchasing private medicine to 'top-up' any state provision. Free market competitive elements could also be mixed with and even favoured within state programmes where practicable, if just results (in terms of equity of access to adequate services) are maintained; and government could see its rôle less as healthcare provider and more as healthcare guarantor or safety-net. But the free market alone cannot be relied upon to distribute health resources justly or efficiently.

5.4 Conclusion

In this chapter we have examined two approaches to healthcare allocation: the *'ad hocery'* which often obtains in practice and the approach of 'leaving it to the market'. Neither has proven adequate to the task of providing a basis for just and efficient allocation of health resources. Clearly if we are to solve some of the problems posed in ways that satisfy the requirements proposed in chapter 4, we shall need to consider more principled, philosophically elaborate approaches to the problem. And it is to some of these that we now turn.

6

The contemporary search for principled solutions (1): What basis for principles?

This chapter briefly surveys and rejects three proposals for the kind of principles which should govern choices about allocation decisions. First is the proposal that the relevant principles should be neutral between different and conflicting understandings of what is required for human flourishing. The aspiration to neutrality has to fail in regard to the allocation of healthcare. For decisions about what kind of healthcare to allocate, to whom, and on what basis, must at least make assumptions about the nature of human persons and what is required for their wellbeing. The second proposal is that we should proceed on the basis of consensus principles. Empirical approaches to identifying such principles are methodologically flawed, but, even were they not, there is no reason to think they would yield rationally defensible principles, of the kind we need, as distinct from unreasonable prejudices. The third proposal is for the adoption of the widely influential 4-principles approach to all bioethical issues. Unfortunately, because the 'principles' are inadequately grounded their scope and application tends to be arbitrary.

6.1 Introduction

In the previous chapter we looked at three ways of effecting healthcare allocation which did not pretend to be based on principled defences of the resulting distribution of resources. In this and the two following chapters we shall examine some more recent and more philosophically sophisticated approaches to these questions recommended by contemporary 'liberal' philosophers. Once again we cannot pretend to survey the whole range of contemporary proposals, and have selected three representative ones for consideration: the 'principlist' approach of many bioethicists; liberal welfarism, which seems philosophically congenial to the original ideals of the NHS (chapter 7); and the utilitarian-economic perspective favoured by some health planners (chapter 8). Before doing so, however, we must consider on what basis one arrives at the relevant principles for allocating healthcare.

6.2 Neutral principles?

If we reject a policy of leaving healthcare distribution to *ad hoc* decisions or to the free market in favour of a more critical and systematic approach it will be necessary to establish principles and criteria. Where are we to get such standards from? This is not the place to review the history and contemporary debates regarding basic ethical theory; however we shall briefly consider some of the points of departure of the theories we examine below.

Many contemporary writers seek 'neutral' ('thin' or 'anti-perfectionist') principles which can be adopted by the state and by people-*qua*-citizens as a public conception of justice in the regulation of a liberal, pluralist society.[1] Such an approach aims to avoid choices between competing conceptions of the good, to allow all to pursue their own diverse views of the good life, and to avoid imposing any particular conception upon people who do not share it. This presumes that people can separate their 'public' and their 'private' lives and they can then be 'neutral' *as citizens* and yet live by a more adequately elaborated ethic in the rest of their lives. But it is doubtful that this would be possible without embracing some kind of moral or psychological schizophrenia, as well as inappropriately narrowing justice to the realm of 'public life'. However we distinguish 'public' from 'private', it will be the same agents, with the same consciences, moral principles and characters, who must work out what to do in various more or less public or private situations, and these two spheres will considerably overlap.

Furthermore, the requirement of 'neutrality' would seem by definition to preclude state involvement in a whole range of worthy activities, including healthcare: after all, citizens differ considerably about what healthcare they want and how it should be allocated; any government tax, provision and rationing scheme would seem to be a case of 'imposing' one conception of the good on people and excluding others, as the free-marketeers complain. In fact, of course, the very existence of the democratic state requires the promotion of a certain conception (or range of conceptions) of the good life and the discouraging or even prohibition of certain others. This is all the clearer the further one goes into the detail of any health system or activity. If a certain level of healthcare (e.g. what is 'necessary', what is preferred...) is to be provided for certain persons (the 'worst-off', those willing to pay, all citizens...) and allocated according to some criterion (equality, age, level of consciousness...), then particular, debateable conception(s) of the human person and of the good of persons will unavoidably be adopted or presumed. Any attempts by the state *not* to arbitrate between or impose any values would in fact favour the *status quo*, allow, protect and encourage certain conceptions of the good rather than others, and leave the state paralysed in the face of crying social needs and problems.[2]

In order to achieve this much sought after 'neutrality', writers commonly propose some imaginary situation in which only considerations thought relevant to the identification of principles of justice are allowed into play. In one famous device for modelling impartiality, 'the Original Position', idealized contractors know the general laws of biology, psychology and society, but are ignorant of their society's stage of development and their own particular natural characteristics, endowments, values and social location; they are rational and cautious; they devise and seek to fulfil their own plans of life; and they want to co-operate in a just and harmonious society. These agents know that there are certain things which people require if they are to achieve their life-plans (liberties, opportunities, income, wealth...) and their simple task is to choose the principles on which to base a social structure which will satisfy them wherever they turn out to be located in it.[3]

Such models of impartiality often seem to be chosen with a view to justifying principles already chosen on some other basis (e.g. that they are the principles which already inform North American society). It is also far from clear how principles derived from such models – in which people are stripped of much of their knowledge, values, commitments and circumstances and presumed to be rational, virtuous, healthy, cooperative and compliant decision-makers – would apply in the real world where people are not like that. Societies are also more complex than these models allow, and commonly resistant to change in some 'ideal' direction. Morality must address these complexities with principles rather more numerous and more substantive than the models presume. As a result, principles of justice appropriate to the real world will differ from those chosen in 'the Original Position' or the like.[4]

6.3 Consensus principles?

Instead of vainly seeking some idealized 'neutral' theory of justice, some writers in recent years have proposed that we aim for a 'majority' or 'consensus' theory of justice, one which systematizes people's sense of justice as expressed in their best considered judgments and their actual practice,[5] or as expressed in an opinion poll. Some health authorities in Britain have polled local people to get some sense of their preferences for healthcare allocation, and in general there is an increasing emphasis on public consultation as an integral element of the commissioning process. In the US state of Oregon, whose health-care priorities scheme we shall examine below (8.3), public preferences were identified through a series of public hearings, surveys, telephone polls, community meetings, consultations of experts, and meetings of commissioners; and QALY studies (to which we shall also return below; 8.2) seek poll information of how people appraise various illnesses or symptom-constellations and how they rank them. Advocates of such approaches claim they yield or at least reflect some sort of majority or consensus account of 'the good life' and thereby avoid idealized, idiosyncratic or prejudiced standards. There are, however, several problems with this.

The principal difficulty with consensus and majority approaches is that they are inclined simply to confirm majority prejudices and reinforce the *status quo*. Empirical studies are apt to reflect cultural prejudices.[6] Any less empirical attempt to construct an implicit consensus view is likely to reflect the intuitions of the writer and his or her social group, and turn political philosophy into cultural anthropology, comparative religion or a confession of faith. In the area of healthcare this is especially problematic: current practices and judgments are probably impossible to sort into a coherent system (they are so inconsistent, fragmentary and *ad hoc*), yet what almost all agree upon is the need for some *rational* canons of criticism and redirection. We properly look to ethics to provide these even if they prove 'divisive' or unpopular.

There are many other problems with polling approaches to health-care allocation. Polling of preferences is still a relatively young 'science' and one which is notoriously dogged with methodological difficulties. Who is asked and what they are asked are crucial. The Oregon Scheme, for instance, obtained its 'popular values' by means of telephone polls (which exclude non-English speakers and many of the poor), public meetings (which were largely attended by 'the worried well': healthy, white, articulate, middle-aged, middle-class people, especially healthworkers) and the government-appointed commissioners (no-one pretended they were a 'representative sample of the population'). QALY studies have tended to rely on even smaller and less representative samples. Different sample groups give very different answers in this field; patients themselves differ considerably from 'outsiders';[7] and there are many reasons to question the validity of anyone making judgments about another person's quality of life. Questions, like sample groups, can be chosen and/or presented naïvely or even with a view to receiving congenial results.

That there is need for considerable caution regarding opinion poll results does not mean that the very idea of polls seeking to identify 'community attitudes' on healthcare priorities is in all respects mis-conceived. The polling in Oregon, for instance, helped to get the issues aired publicly, to get more people to form and express a view about them, and was undoubtedly a useful aid to democratic decision-making. Special care must be taken, however, not further to marginalize the views and ultimately the persons of vulnerable and inarticulate minorities; and to avoid simply confirming passing fashions, popular prejudices or the views of the influential. The need for a principled critique of the views of the majority remains, as does the need for appropriate exercise of authority by those charged with leadership in the community.[8]

6.4 Arbitrary principles?

Perhaps out of despair of achieving any neutral or consensus principles for healthcare allocation, some writers simply assert a series of rules or standards without offering any coherent basis for their adoption. 'Prin-ciplism' – the approach favoured by many contemporary medical ethicists[9] – would seem to be an example of this. According to this approach there are (currently) four *prima facie* 'principles' of healthcare ethics: (respect for) autonomy, beneficence, nonmaleficence and justice. [A fifth principle, truth-telling, fell out of the list in the early 1980s.[10] Other principles, such as reverence for life and the duty to keep promises, have been included by some but excluded by other writers.] The philosophical basis of these principles remains obscure, but moral dilemmas are seen as arising because of conflicts between them.[11] As a result the principles must be 'prioritized', 'balanced' or otherwise compromised – though for the most part 'autonomy' trumps all the others.

Because the 'principles' are ill-grounded and their relationship to each other vague they fail to inform decision-making in a non-arbitrary way. In consequence, 'principlist' discussions of healthcare allocation which invoke a 'principle of justice' fail to provide specific guidance for action. The 'principle' is invoked in a way that tends to function as one on a checklist of concerns, a kind of consciousness-raising slogan, code for 'consider whether your healthcare decision is fair'. In doing this the principlists recommend fairness without really explaining what it is. Often there is included a neat summary of competing theories of justice from which the reader is invited to choose according to personal taste, though little is said about how one should choose or how the theories would be applied to real life questions such as the allocation of healthcare resources. Further difficulties arise when considering the healthcare allocation question because of the simplistic consequentialism of some of the principlists.[12]

By contrasting the value or principle of 'justice' with that of 'beneficence' the principlists characterize allocations which fail to respect the dignity and reasonable expectations of others, (and are thus *unjust* in terms of the account we shall propose in Part III), as merely a shortfall in 'beneficence', 'charity' or 'generosity'. We shall argue that distributional choices or systems can attack or at least fail appropriately to promote the good of individuals and their 'common good' precisely because they are deficient in fellow-feeling, self-giving and joint effort to satisfy needs and promote the flourishing of all, and that this deficiency is ultimately one in justice. We shall further argue that to view the requirements of friendship or charity as 'optional' or to define what is 'due' to others too narrowly is to impoverish moral understanding.

To this narrow concept of justice (which they call a single principle) the principlists oppose their three other principles: beneficence, non-maleficence and autonomy. Accordingly, questions such as the giving of 'treatments' (including abortion) and the withholding of treatment (even with euthanasiast intent) are treated by this school under these three heads rather than as questions of 'justice'. In keeping with contemporary Western individualism, 'social justice' then receives a last, 'also-ran' position: we decide first what is 'best' for the patient *qua*-individual-distinct-from-community, and only then ask whether it is socially damaging. We will call this model of bioethical decision-making into question. Rather than relying upon neutrality, consensus or the arbitrary selection of rules, we shall offer a coherent theory from which to derive and in which to situate genuine moral principles applicable to the allocation of healthcare. But first we must examine the two leading contemporary accounts of the basis upon which healthcare should be directly distributed.

7

The contemporary search for principled solutions (2): Liberal-welfarist approaches

The ideals of the NHS may seem to have their congruent under-pinnings in contemporary liberal-welfarist understandings of the requirements of social justice. Contemporary liberal-welfarism emphasises principles of liberty, equality and fraternity. But it is also committed to neutrality about the human good. And that leaves welfarism too underdetermined to provide an adequate framework for healthcare resource allocation. An emphasis on liberty/autonomy without reference to a substantive (non-neutral) understanding of the goods of human flourishing will fail to provide adequate criteria for distinguishing those exercises of autonomy which are consistent with the individual and common good from those which are not. And the aim of providing a level of healthcare sufficient to secure equality of opportunity cannot be adequately specified without a substantive under-standing of the human good which answers the question 'Opportunity for what?' Finally, the ideal of fraternity, which looks to provide for those in 'greatest need', also requires to be informed by a substantive understanding of the human good if the relevant needs are to be adequately identified and efforts to meet them kept consistent with provision for other genuine needs.

7.1 'Health for all' – the traditional NHS approach

The founding principle of the NHS, and the one upon which it has

45

operated until now, was 'health for all' – universal access to comprehensive, cradle-to-grave healthcare, irrespective of any factor other
than healthcare need. In the words of Aneurin Bevan, the Minister
of Health at the time of the inception of the health service, it would
'universalize the best'. Underpinning this commitment were a
number of values expressed not only in political manifestos and in
public policy statements such as the *Beveridge Report*, but also in the
day-to-day practice of the NHS: the moral equality of persons; a
high value placed on human life, health and welfare; a strong sense
of solidarity between citizens; a special concern for the worst off;
and respect for human rights.

Prima facie at least, these values are broadly consistent with the positions proposed by several leading 'liberal' political philosophers at the
more 'egalitarian' or 'welfarist' end of the spectrum. These writers
commonly propose three principles:

- *liberty*: freedom should be maximized for all and only limited
  where necessary for the sake of protecting freedom itself or
  for satisfying those basic needs which the exercise of liberty
  requires;
- *equality*: there is a presumption in favour of socioeconomic equality and inequalities should be admitted only if this is ultimately to
  the advantage of all; and
- *fraternity*: there should be a general concern for the common
  good and special provision should be made for the welfare of
  those members of the community who are disadvantaged.

In Part III we shall propose a framework for healthcare allocation
which has a place for all these 'liberal' values. A major problem
with specifically 'liberal' accounts, however, is that they generally
focus only on the distribution of wealth, income and certain other
social opportunities such as employment: healthcare does not normally
feature among their distributable goods.[1] This is because these writers
seek the kind of 'neutral' account criticized above: they are concerned
to identify only those all-purpose goods which are instrumental to
everyone's lifeplans, refusing to say whether things as basic as life,
health and friendship, and the means to enjoying them, should be
part of everyone's objects and commitments. The NHS, however,
begins with the assumption that health and (appropriate) healthcare
are goods 'for all', and that a community such as the UK should
ensure that all have access to them.

7.2 *Liberty* above all: the contemporary idolization of autonomy

'Liberal' political philosophers commonly place the ideal of self-determination or autonomy highest among their values, and this has affected medical ethics, healthcare policy and practice in many ways too. A high view of the 'professional autonomy' of the doctor has traditionally bolstered resistance to political or managerial interference in medical practice; a similarly high view of the proper autonomy of the patient has grounded the growing emphasis on informed consent and patient-advocacy, and growing hostility to 'medical paternalism'; and most recently an exaggerated view of the importance of self-determination has fuelled calls for 'reproductive liberty', for euthanasia, and the like. In chapter 5 we noted the pre-eminence of this motif in contemporary advocacy of a freer market in healthcare, and in 6.4 its ascendancy in 'principlist' bioethics; but autonomy also looms large in most democratic welfare-oriented perspectives, and after two decades of domination by this theme, only recently have bioethicists come to question the presumed priority or 'trumping power' of autonomy over all other moral concerns in healthcare.

'Autonomy above all' is a doctrine which has its attractions. It appears to show great respect for human freedom and for differences of opinion. It precludes various 'paternalistic' healthcare proposals, even if they promise 'efficiency' in the use of resources – e.g. treating competent patients without their consent, public health measures such as dietary laws, compulsory blood transfusions, compulsory abortions for handicap, or the quarantining of all HIV carriers. It encourages people to take responsibility for their own health and healthcare. It helps to identify what is wrong with proposals such as compulsory organ redistribution. And it is consistent with the right of those healthcare providers who conscientiously object to taking part in certain procedures.

But there are difficulties with any unqualified emphasis on self-determination. First, if the autonomy of all patients is to be respected, conflicts will inevitably arise because patients will have competing expectations and demands. The area of resource allocation is a prime example: even were consent the only moral issue in giving treatments, any shortfall of supply will require choices and the frustration of some people's preferences. Secondly, if the autonomy of both patients *and health professionals* is to be respected, further conflicts will be unavoidable. Communication, compromise, shared decision-making, and

47

perhaps the exercise of some legitimate authority, will be required within a framework of common purposes and agreed procedures. And in an area like healthcare this will require rather more than contracts and recognized rights and duties of non-interference.

Furthermore, the healthcare relationship is not a simple one of two autonomous contracting individuals. The parties to healthcare do not in general operate like parties to other economic bargains. On the one hand, the patient is severely restricted in terms of freedom (he or she may be desperate, confused, intimidated, unconscious . . .), knowledge (not understanding the condition, treatment options, costs and bene-fits . . .) and rationality (for immaturity, disability, disease, pain, fear, moods and drugs can severely limit this). On the other hand, the healthworker is also confined by the state of the art, professional expectations, legal requirements, decisions by health managers, resource constraints, and so on. The association between patient and healthworker is also one of very unequal power, and despite recent efforts to encourage patients to take greater responsibility for their own health and healthcare, many still prefer to leave much of the deci-sion-making to the 'experts'. Health professionals are in a position in which, were they limited only by their own right of self-determination and a duty not to interfere with the autonomy of others capable of exercising rational choice, they may considerably over-treat or under-treat at least some of their patients out of self-interest or some other motive. Thus the doctor-patient relationship has traditionally been understood as a fiduciary (trustee-beneficiary) or covenant relationship with certain intrinsic duties of action and restraint, rather than a relationship of contract between provider and purchaser.

Even were agents all well-informed, free and independent, it is by no means clear that by being 'left to their own devices' in pursuit of their own preferences or desires they would best achieve the good life (whatever that might be). Sometimes their choices will involve inconsistency with the rest of their own conception of the good or be manifestly self-destructive (on almost any account of the good); sometimes their choices may manifest disrespect for themselves, for others, for the common good or for moral reason. Freedom, properly understood, is the ability to choose well, to act with a view to the flourishing of persons and communities, not a licence to 'do whatever one pleases'. Liberty to exercise this ability and opportunity for self-expression remain important, but precisely because free choosing and what we make of ourselves by our choices are indispensable to normal human flourishing. Without a richer account of what such flourishing would involve, the appeal to 'liberty above all' (the autonomy trump) appears to attach as much value to self-destructive absence of restraint as to freedom from real impediments to flourishing.

7.3 *Equality*: equitable access to healthcare so as to ensure roughly equal life opportunities

Many people believe that healthcare should be distributed *equally*, as a requisite or expression of equal concern and respect. But 'equally' in regard to what? Equal access may be the appropriate standard for initial contact and diagnosis; equal provision may be the appropriate standard for some public health measures (e.g. vaccinations, fluoridation), as well as for some health promotion programmes; but a strictly equal distribution cannot be the standard for treatments generally. Most of us do not want or need blood transfusions, organ transplants or hospital beds most of the time, and it would clearly be inappropriate if such resources were allocated on a *per capita per annum* basis. Various standards of equality have therefore been proposed. One is: *access to whatever is necessary for equal opportunities or life chances.* According to this view provision for basic human needs such as healthcare and education should be made so as to ensure, as far as possible, that people receive what is necessary and effective for maintaining them at, restoring them to, or at least helping them approach, the normal range of opportunities to devise, revise and pursue their own commitments and life-plans.[2] On this account human beings have a fundamental interest in establishing institutions such as health systems which enable the enjoyment of such an opportunity range for all, without financial, racial, geographical or other morally inappropriate barriers.

This approach has important points of contact with that elaborated by us in Part III. But it is not without its problems. How can we judge what level of health and healthcare provision is required for enjoyment of the 'normal' range of opportunities in life if we adopt a 'neutral' position which avoids substantive conceptions of human nature and the good(s) pursued by persons in community? How are we to weight healthcare against educational, occupational or other opportunities which are also necessary for people to enjoy the 'normal' range of opportunities? Is healthcare to have priority over all else? Does health have some value(s) to us in addition to what it contributes to our opportunities to make plans and choices? Does healthcare seek and express more than the achievement of normal opportunity ranges (e.g. solidarity with those who suffer, the values of the Hippocratic tradition...)?[3] Moderate liberalism has too 'thin' a conception of the person and the community to be able to answer such questions satisfactorily.

Nonetheless, the equal opportunity goal does provide some direction. It suggests that what is allocatable as healthcare should, as far as possible, be sufficient to cater for the healthcare needs of all those whose life-chances are prejudiced by illness. It suggests that need (though not necessarily need alone) should be the basis of allocational choices, and that a number of other allocational criteria (such as those examined in chapter 12) should be excluded. Thus there will be a *prima facie* case of injustice in healthcare allocation if people in an affluent community lack access to care appropriate to their needs, or if finite health resources are distributed on some basis such as racial or ethnic group, beliefs, gender, sexual orientation, social or regional location, social contribution, disability and quality of life, intelligence and articulateness, attractiveness, co-operativeness, or ability to pay.[4]

How would one operationalize the equal life-opportunities goal in healthcare? One method would be to apportion the available resources equally – not among the population as a whole, which we have seen would be absurd, but among those already assessed as in need and likely to benefit (in life-opportunity terms) from the resource. Once again, this may work with some therapies (e.g. giving all those recuperating from a particular operation roughly the same number of hours of physiotherapy); but more often than not equal shares will not work because the therapy concerned will not be divisible (one cannot share a kidney-for-transplant between five candidates) or will be divisible but would be useless if so divided (e.g. giving each of five patients one hour every five hours in an ICU). There will be many situations where an either/or choice has to be made, whether between institutions, wards, doctors, therapies or patients. Preference would presumably be given to those patients whose life-opportunities were most gravely or urgently imperilled. There would then be three possible ways of operationalizing equal opportunity among those in roughly equal need: (a) for-all-or-for-none, i.e. if not all who would benefit can have the therapy in question, then it will not be provided; (b) some sort of lottery; or (c) first-come-first-served (a queue). Were a finite resource given to some who would benefit but not to others, then healthcare would only exacerbate inequalities in life-opportunities: thus a for-all-or-for-none policy would seem to be favoured. On the other hand, were a lottery or first-come-first-served policy used, at least some would be thereby brought nearer the normal opportunity range, there would be fewer outside it, and none would have been discriminated against. (We shall consider the objections that may well be raised to all three strategies in chapter 12.)

7.4 *Fraternity*: should special provision be made for the healthcare of the disadvantaged?

In later chapters we shall see that Christian social teaching supports the provision of special care, including healthcare, for the disadvantaged (chapter 15) and that a secular natural law case can be made for this too as an expression of fraternity or social solidarity (chapters 11 and 14). Some contemporary liberal-welfarist writers have come to a similar conclusion on the basis of their principle that any inequalities in the allocation of basic social goods are to be arranged so that they are to the benefit of the least advantaged. Although some have thought that this would require equal access to healthcare irrespective of position or background, the principle actually allows significant inequalities where these would benefit the worst-off.[5] Most likely a two-tiered health system with universal provision for people's genuine healthcare needs and a free market thereafter would be indicated, rather than stricter equality. A stronger version of this proposal would 'positively discriminate' in favour of those who are disadvantaged in terms of health or access to healthcare. This would require a 'third tier' of special programmes to address the needs of particular groups, such as those with disabilities, chronic ailments, low birthweight and so on.

A principle of preference for the disadvantaged can, however, lead to some very counter-intuitive conclusions such as always preferring a small benefit for a few of the worst-off to giving even very large benefits to even very large numbers of the marginally better-off.[6] Furthermore, if health and need for healthcare is to be a crucial part of this approach, there must be much more unpacking of the notion of a *need* than most 'neutral' liberals are willing to undertake. 'Thin' theories of the good once again leave us unable to resolve such matters other than by polling or arbitration.

7.5 Advantages and disadvantages of the liberal-welfarist approach

Moderate liberal approaches to justice emphasize certain key values: impartiality, respect for autonomy and diversity, an involved but non-paternalistic state, equal respect, special concern for the most disadvantaged, social harmony, and a public conception of justice – these are all rightly stressed and will be taken up again in chapters 9–14. While broadly compatible with the inspiration and practice of the NHS to date, these theories also invite its improvement in various ways.

But recurring difficulties emerge with any attempt to derive a clear direction for healthcare allocation from these theories. Like the free-marketeers, these writers commonly assume a simplistic and unsituated account of autonomy. Their accounts of the demands of equality and fraternity prove too 'thin' to take us very far in answering questions such as: whether it is possible and advisable for the state to remain neutral about healthcare; how should one order the various liberal values and principles; whether healthcare is properly an opportunity or a primary good subject to liberal principles of justice; what are the nature and normative implications of 'needs'; what are the proper ends of the practice of medicine; and what place do familial and community life and shared values have in determining allocation.

One final problem with the liberal-welfarist account should be noted at this stage. Where healthcare is to be allocated so as to raise (as far as possible) those with less than the normal opportunity range to within that range, almost unlimited allocations to healthcare would be required, especially for those with grave disabilities and diseases; if healthcare were to be distributed to the advantage of those worst-off in terms of health and healthcare access, very considerable redistribution of resources would likewise be required in most societies. On the face of it such 'egalitarian' distributive principles could place an enormous demand on social resources, even reducing the whole society to penury. Awareness of this problem has led moderate liberals to propose several limits.

The first is that only services which are strictly 'healthcare' should be included – a matter to which we adverted in chapter 1 when we considered what healthcare is (1.3). The second is that socioeconomic realities must be taken into account: societies and their health systems, institutions and workers only have responsibilities relative to their capacities. The third is that priority should be given to those with health conditions which involve the 'greatest' threat to liberty or self-esteem or the greatest curtailment of opportunity range, and to persons who are most 'severely' disadvantaged overall or specifically with regard to health and access to healthcare. And the fourth is that various democratic procedures may be adopted to sort popular views and achieve a consensus or at least an authoritative decision on priorities. All this said, liberals are still faced with a theory which, if it recognises any healthcare rights and duties at all, seems to propose almost infinite ones with little direction on how to limit or sort them. Once again, a richer account of the good of persons in community would seem to be required.

8

The contemporary search for principled solutions (3): Utilitarian-economic approaches

This chapter is concerned with exclusively utilitarian approaches to allocation, i.e. ones which characteristically depend on placing a quantitative value on the quality-of-life benefits of healthcare interventions. A host of problems attend this undertaking, of which two of the most fundamental are: (1) the problem of what to identify as 'benefits', and (2) the problem of either ranking or assigning commensurable values to qualitatively disparate benefits. The second problem is irresolvable, so that it is impossible to have a calculus of benefits which could form the *objective* basis for resource allocation. Furthermore, exclusive reliance on a policy of utility maximization in healthcare allocation will prove contrary to the requirements of justice, as well as leaving no place for respect for other values of fundamental importance to the practice of healthcare.

8.1 Introduction

An alternative, utilitarian account of justice in healthcare allocation has been proposed in recent years by some philosophers and economists and has found favour among some healthcare policy makers and administrators. According to this approach an allocative decision, disposition, policy, institution or pattern is to be preferred over its alternatives if it promises to produce the best net sum of benefits and costs (good consequences minus bad consequences). The two most outstanding examples of attempts to apply utilitarianism to healthcare allocation have been the 'Quality-Adjusted Life Years' ('QALYs') model proposed by a number of economists and others,[1] and the systematic application of similar thinking in the scheme devised for and eventually implemented in the US state of Oregon and recommended by some for more universal application.[2]

Supporters of these schemes emphasize their benefits such as: stretching the health pound to provide more services for more people; guaranteeing that more important services will be included in any minimum package; allowing for the elimination of less important services, especially ineffective and only marginally beneficial ones; open debate and community involvement in setting priorities; visible criteria which exclude arbitrary or hidden standards; greater fiscal restraint and government responsibility for spending taxpayers' money as effectively and efficiently as possible; and overall a more rational basis for healthcare allocation than the *status quo*. In the analysis that follows we shall question whether the supposed advantages of these utilitarian schemes are in fact achieved or achievable; but more importantly, whether they are achievable in ways which are just. But first we must outline what precisely has been attempted in these projects in applied utilitarianism in healthcare allocation.

8.2 Applied utilitarianism (A): QALYs

The QALYs model is held by its proponents to provide several things: a suitable model for assessing the usefulness of a range of healthcare interventions; an action guide for individual choices between alternative healthcare options; and a basis for rational policymaking and management with regard to the allocation of finite health resources. First, the years of life and quality of life yielded by various healthcare interventions are established from clinical data. These are then assessed according to a psychometric index along which one year of life in normal (or perfect) health is valued at 1 QALY, death at 0 QALYs, and one year of life in less than perfect health at less than 1 QALY and greater or less than 0 (death). The cost of achieving one QALY is calculated and a value-for-money ranking is then possible. Rational decision-making is presumed to follow such a ranking. Thus it has been estimated that in terms of cost per QALY cholesterol testing and diet therapy for middle-aged people, neurosurgery for head injury and GP advice to stop smoking are twice to six times as good value for money as antihypertensive therapy to prevent stroke, pacemaker implantation, hip replacement or heart valve replacement, up to 80 times better than coronary artery bypass, kidney transplant, breast screening or heart transplant, up to 120 times as good as dialysis, and several hundred times better than neurosurgery for brain tumour.[3]

8.3 Applied utilitarianism (B): The Oregon Scheme

The only attempt to apply QALYs in a systematic way across the board in a healthcare system has been in Oregon.[4] In an effort to spread the Medicare dollar more broadly across the disadvantaged and to prioritize services provided, the legislature appointed a Commission to rank health services 'by priority from the most important to the least important representing the comparative benefits of each service to the entire population to be served.' In Phase One the Commission decided to use a 'quality of well being' scale, combined with data about costs of treatments and duration of benefit,[5] in order to produce QALY statistics on over 1,600 health services (with certain exclusions[6]) and to hold a series of public hearings to elicit testimony on public values. The provisional QALYs list which followed was full of anomalies: cosmetic surgery had a higher place than repair of an open fracture of the femur; tooth straightening ranked above treatment for Hodgkin's disease; infertility treatment was far above all of these and even above obstetric care for the already-pregnant. In Phase Two the Commissioners chose 17 categories of health conditions and effects of treatment and ranked them from 'essential' to 'very important' to 'valuable to certain individuals'. Over 700 condition-treatment pairs were then assigned to one of the categories (certain services again being excluded); these pairs were then ranked by a mathematical procedure similar to the one used in Phase One but with less weight attached to cost and more to duration and quality of life; once the list was devised the Commissioners corrected it 'by hand' using a 'reasonableness' test to adjust any 'misplaced' services. Actuaries then calculated the costs of providing each service to the estimated number of Medicaid recipients requiring the services. Finally the list was published. Ranked 'essential' were: first, treatments for acute, potentially fatal conditions such as appendicitis and head injury, myocarditis or bacterial meningitis;

then maternity, neonatal and paediatric care; next, treatments for chronic, potentially fatal, conditions; then family planning services, palliative care and preventive care such as dental cleaning and flouride, mammograms and blood pressure screening. Ranked 'very important' were treatments for acute or chronic conditions which are not potentially fatal, such as therapies for vaginitis, migraine and asthma, tooth fillings, hip replacements and cornea repair. Ranked 'valuable to some' were treatments which expedite recovery, infertility services, and less effective treatments such as those for endstage AIDS patients and very low birthweight babies. The budget voted by the state allowed Medicare coverage of the first 587 ranked pairs, i.e. for 98% of all 'essential' services and 82% of all 'very important' services, but only 7% of services 'considered valuable to certain individuals'.

8.4 Which benefits, which losses?

If a utilitarian calculus is to be attempted in the assessment of competing healthcare procedures, policies or patients, it is necessary to predict the benefits and costs of each contending option. But there is a long history of division even among utilitarians themselves over what is to count as a benefit, whether it is things that contribute to greater pleasure (and less pain) for those affected, or to the fulfilment of the most or the strongest of their preferences, or which make for more complex satisfactions, all-round 'happiness' or 'well-being'. It is common today for utilitarians to 'launder' preferences which are to be satisfied, counting some more 'worthy' than others (e.g. 'higher' over 'brutish' pleasures, objective needs or higher order interests over wants and luxuries), including only the preferences of the fully informed, rational, prudent, compassionate, socially concerned agent; they discount preferences which undermine a person's deepest interests, and those motivated bv irrational or anti-social desires (sadism, anger, malice, envy etc.), as well as expensive tastes, and so on. The complexity of deciding what is to count as a benefit and a loss, even before attempting to assess them, highlights the naïvete of one QALY theorist's claim that healthcare rationing requires only two things: a 'technical' judgment by doctors as to which treatments provide the 'biggest bang for the buck' and a 'social' judgment by politicians as to 'how far down this league table' to fund.[7] In fact any judgment as to 'benefit', 'quality of life' (or 'bang') will be irremediably value-laden and not merely 'technical', just as is the judgment that the proper object of healthcare or a health system is to maximize 'bangs for bucks' however assessed. As several commentators in parallel contexts have demonstrated, it is simply incoherent to approach such questions as if there were no evaluative question at all, merely 'brute facts' which are alleged to be observable and measurable independently of evaluation or even as if it were perfectly clear to everyone what are the values involved.

This does not mean, of course, that the search for an account of benefit and loss is futile or unnecessary: healthcare, like all human activities, has certain aims, goods or ends, and to understand the activity and assess it both technically and morally one must understand the benefits it seeks. The identification of some standard(s) of benefit and loss remains an important task. While some utilitarians resort to the satisfaction or frustration of expressed preferences as the sole standard of benefit and loss for healthcare allocation as for all other questions, most at least implicitly recognize some 'internal' or 'objective' ends of healthcare. Thus the Oregon Commission abandoned the first phase of QALY rankings and 'corrected' by hand its second phase according to some (unspecified) notion of what is 'reasonable' in healthcare. QALY theorists take for granted that extension of life, the improvement of health, and health-related gains in quality of life are the goals of healthcare. We shall now examine these in turn.

Early attempts to measure health status for welfare and development purposes measured benefit in terms of life expectancy, infant mortality and reported rates of specific diseases. In particular, lives saved and disease or disability prevented or cured were regarded as the best tests of the effectiveness of health and welfare programmes. One leading British critic of QALYs from within a utilitarian perspective insists that what matters to people is being alive (and all that allows): it is lives that are valuable to people, not quality of life adjusted years, and thus the fewer lives that are lost prematurely the better.[8] Others argue that it is the business of medicine to save life, maximize life-years, and maintain health – all with no quality considerations. Cost-effectiveness analysts rely upon 'objective' health profiles and make their assessments in terms of 'health gain per unit cost'; most QALY analysis likewise relies on various health indices.

Leaving aside the question of whether it is the proper function of medicine to maximize lives or life-years (without reference to health improved) or to maintain or restore health (without reference to quality of life), we may still ask: is the extension of life or the restoration of health always a benefit, and is it equally so for all persons? In chapter 9 we shall argue that life and health are always intrinsic goods, even if the extension of life and the restoration of health are not always morally required (9.2). But utilitarians and 'value of life' economists commonly deny that life and health are of themselves benefits: they argue that these goods are merely prerequisites to other values such as certain conscious experiences, the possession of exercisable capacities, or realisable life-plans. On this account there can be such a thing as 'a life not worth living' or health not worth having: the pain and suffering in a person's life can outweigh the pleasure and happiness. (Others also will be better or worse off were the person dead but, as we shall see below, QALY theorists would exclude such 'externalities'.) On this account sometimes death is a benefit, life and health a loss.

On a consistent utilitarian view, therefore, life and health are not necessarily benefits, and death and sickness not necessarily losses, and when they are they are not equally so for everyone. Is good or improved *quality of life* to be regarded as the benefit, then, and poor or worsened quality of life to be regarded as the loss? *Prima facie* quality of life would seem to be a crucial aspect of welfare. QALY theorists point out that medicine has always properly focussed on more than just maximizing the number of lives saved, or years added to lives, or even objective health gains: its traditional and contemporary emphasis has been on these things *and* on improving people's quality of life: hence palliative care, pain management, and a great many healthcare practices aimed at respecting patient dignity and improving comfort and self-esteem. A single-minded concern to prolong life or improve health can well be unreasonable (as we too shall argue in chapter 9), brings medicine into disrepute, and can lead to suffering and despair. Furthermore, when assessing whether a treatment is 'beneficial', 'extraordinary' or 'disproportionately burdensome', doctor and patient will naturally and quite properly take into account its effects on the patient's quality of life.

But QALY theorists assume (as do most other analysts of cost-benefit and cost-effectiveness of healthcare) that a gain in health-related quality of life is always a benefit and that this is the only benefit of healthcare. Such a claim is dubious even from a utilitarian perspective. Healthcare obviously serves a number of values (and has a number of costs) irreducible to health-related quality of life for the patient, and these are left out of any QALY calculus. (For example, without restored health one may not be able to carry out certain intellectual tasks, but the quality of one's thinking would not be counted in a QALY calculation.) Nor will a utilitarian account sustain the QALY theorists' claim that one QALY is equally valuable whoever enjoys it. As we have already noted, there is overwhelming evidence that people value different quality of life states differently: some accommodate heroically to terribly reduced quality of life; others suffer enormously (or imagine they do) from the slightest reduction of their quality of life. That different people are willing to take different risks with their health-related quality of life or to spend more or less of their resources on healthcare (and thus obtain or forego other things) is strong evidence that they do not value QALYs equally. Strict utilitarianism, therefore, cannot stop at asking 'how many QALYs and at what cost?' (as does the QALY accountant) but must also ask 'what other benefits and for whom?' Even in utilitarian terms, utilitarian healthcare allocation projects have so far failed to base their assessments on an adequate account of the value of life, health and all that healthcare attempts to serve.

8.5 Problems with counting benefits and losses

Let us suspend for now any disbelief in the accounts of benefit and loss proposed by the utilitarians, especially by the QALY theorists, and accept that there is some coherent and identifiable class of benefit and loss from healthcare and that this is all that is at issue in allocation decisions. How are these benefits and losses to be measured and counted? On the face of it this seems fairly straightforward: we compare a patient sample who receive the treatment in question with a similar patient sample who do not. We ascertain as objectively and accurately as possible whether (on average, in most cases...), increased numbers of lives are saved, years of life added, health improved, and/or health-related quality of life enhanced. We can make similar comparisons regarding broader or narrower classes of person and therapy and regarding institutions, policies and systems.

But how are these outcomes of therapies to be calculated and compared? Here healthcare economics meets certain hard realities: there is in fact very little scientifically reliable evidence of treatment outcomes and appropriateness; such research as there is is so rudimentary, slow, cumbersome and expensive as to offer little hope of a sound research base for prioritization on the basis of outcomes; most clinical interventions currently performed by physicians have not been subjected and are unlikely ever to be subjected to scientifically adequate controlled trials. The Oregon Commission found that the impressive (and intimidating) array of mathematical formulas offered by the health economists lacked an adequate information base; they had to supplement the scant outcomes literature with the opinions of panels of health professionals and with their own corrections 'by hand'; intuition ('guestimate') soon became more important than mathematics.[9] The problem with this is that the judgments of healthworkers about outcomes are far from reliable, even when they are being as objective and altruistic in their assessments as possible.

There are also theoretical difficulties with the very notion of estimating healthcare outcomes. If the benefit to be measured is lives saved or life-years added (measures which will obviously apply only to life-saving therapies), there are difficulties in assessing cause and effect so as to determine what is actually to be attributed to the therapy in question, especially where no (untreated) control group is available. How are we to value the lives saved? Economists have proposed various ways of expressing the value of life in monetary terms. Most popular have been the Discounted Future Earnings or Human Capital approach, which equates the value of life with the subject's future earnings stream, and the Willingness To Pay approach, which looks to what people are willing to pay to reduce a risk of death, or what they would accept as compensation for an increased risk of death. Apart from the philosophical difficulties with the very notion of valuing lives, these measures represent a fairly impoverished view of the value of life even from a utilitarian perspective. There is much more to life than income, and the risks people take with their lives tell us more about their moral, intellectual and emotional dispositions (and their personal and socioeconomic circumstances) than about how much they do, or we should, value those lives.[10]

Most treatments are aimed not at saving lives or life-years but at improvements in health or quality of life. But how are benefits such as improved life-expectancy, cure of disease, pain and symptom relief, improved mobility etc., to be measured or even ranked ordinally, especially when there may be various mixtures and tradeoffs between these benefits and the burdens of treatment? Is curing or circumventing infertility a greater or lesser benefit than curing pain and immobility through a hip replacement operation? Health economists have sought to overcome these difficulties by providing an impressive armoury of health profiles (multidimensional indices of characteristics such as pain, sleep disturbance, ability to perform particular activities, social interaction, emotional reactions, etc.,) which can be used to compare patients before and after treatment. QALY theorists then seek to apply quality of life judgments to these various health statuses, using the 'Short Form 36', the 'EuroQol', the 'Index of Well-Being', the 'York-Rosser-Watts Quality of Life Index', and so on. Following the methods described above, the QALY theorist then values one year of life in normal (or perfect?) health at 1 QALY and all lesser health-related quality of life states at some value less than one (or, if worse than death, less than zero); the QALY value of a treatment is the number of QALYs the patient can look forward to with the treatment minus the number the patient can look forward to if untreated.

What these writers fail to establish, however, is that the range of benefits from healthcare – whether conceived in broad utilitarian terms or more narrowly in QALYs – are sufficiently alike in meaning to allow their reduction to some single factor for the purposes of cardinal measurement or even, less ambitiously, for an ordinal ranking. Individuals *do*, of course, adopt various personal hierarchies for measuring and ranking diverse goods: but few would pretend that these are rationally compelling or 'objective' when the goods concerned are of their nature incommensurable.[11] Even were many people to agree on their priorities in this area (and the intractability of healthcare allocation dilemmas to date makes this seem unlikely), this may simply mean that they share similar temperaments, or prejudices, or social conditioning. Our efforts at such assessments merely reveal *our inclinations*. Likewise in healthcare: how many lives saved are equal to how many with considerably improved health? how much pain removed is equal to a gain in mobility or social interaction? and so on. Polling techniques may tell us roughly *what some people feel* about these trade-offs, and even the personal standards by which they would make such choices for themselves; but they cannot provide an ethically commanding rule for others (or even necessarily for themselves) unless *all* the 'good' in one particular option is *in one and the same sense* contained in the other being compared with it, *plus or minus* some (one) thing else.

Incommensurability, then, radically restricts the applicability of any calculus of benefits.[12] This does not mean that choices in healthcare allocation are unavoidably arbitrary or whimsical: in chapters 9 to 14 we shall examine the sorts of values, principles, virtues, criteria and commitments which should shape choices between reasonable options. *But incommensurability does mean that the utilitarian dream of achieving some mathematical basis for such choices which every reasonable person will or should agree upon is illusory.*

Were such commensuration possible, however, there would not, strictly speaking, be any choices to be made: for the 'more beneficial proposal overall' would be the only one which attracted the rational agent. If one could demonstrate that stopping renal transplantation and putting the resources towards hip replacements would contribute to an objectively better state of affairs then no rational person would oppose it. But in reality, of course, we *do* have to make hard choices and we have to make them precisely because there are diverse and irreducible goods and evils at stake in both proposals. The notion of the 'greater net good overall' has no definite meaning *antecedent to* the choice which ends deliberation: it is in the act of choice itself that one determines whether one will be the sort of person for whom lifeextension *or* pain-reduction shall be *the* greater good.[13]

Apart from incommensurability, there are a number of other difficulties with utilitarian attempts to count benefits and losses in healthcare as elsewhere: problems with interpersonal comparisons, problems with effects stretching unpredictably into an indefinite future, problems of assessing and comparing risks, conflicts between subjective and objective benefits of healthcare, and the impracticability of relying upon averages of benefits when patients vary enormously in their response to therapies. There are also a whole range of methodological complications which we need not rehearse here.

8.6 Justice and other values

Let us assume for the purposes of critical discussion that there *is* some way of measuring the benefits and losses of various treatments, non-treatment, and so on, as the utilitarian asserts. What then? For the utilitarian healthcare planner there is only one simple rule: offer the treatments (etc.) which promise the best and cheapest overall outcome both for the sick and for others affected. Or as the health economist puts it: seek to equate marginal benefits and marginal costs so that the last pound's worth of resources devoted to healthcare increases the human satisfaction by more or by exactly the same amount as the same pound's worth devoted to any other healthcare project. Or, as the QALY accountant puts it: maximize health-related QALYs gained with the budget you have.[14] Some contemporary administrators, health economists and bioethicists have accepted this approach more or less uncritically.[15] At the risk of considerable simplification, one can say that the logic of utilitarian approaches favours policies something like the following:

- health promotion (where efficient) and cheaper healthcare technologies are to be preferred to expensive curative treatments;
- expensive or scarce healthcare technologies are only to be available to the young and those who are likely to lead long productive lives;
- in competition for resources, preference should be given to those likely to receive the greatest benefit in terms of improved length and quality of life and to those likely to make the greatest future social contribution;
- as far as possible, only short-term services are to be provided, with longer-term custodial or institutional care reduced;
- healthcare for the terminally ill, dying, elderly, chronically sick or incapacitated, severely handicapped, and permanently unconscious, is to be given lowest priority or eliminated.

Even if we agree that healthcare should in general be distributed with a view to maximizing aggregate health gains ('the biggest bang for the buck') we must ask: should we do so *no matter what*? In chapters 9 to 14 we shall argue that respect for individuals, for basic values, and for the norms of common morality such as the prohibition on killing the innocent, will exclude some allocations which otherwise might appear to be rational and efficient. Here it will be sufficient to consider just a few of the conclusions which the logic of utility maximization in healthcare allocation may be deemed to require.[16]

One way of increasing QALYs would be to bring more and more people into the world (at least up to a total very much greater than that reached so far): with this in mind all methods of family limitation might be forbidden, resources focussed upon infertility treatment, antenatal and neonatal care, preference given to women of child-bearing age and to girls over boys, all with a view to maximizing birth-rates. Another way would be always to prefer the person with the longer life-expectancy, such as 22-year-olds over 23-year-olds, women over men of the same age, certain ethnic groups, those with a genetic predisposition to greater longevity, and so on. Persons might be tested or treated without consent (e.g. compulsorily aborted if carrying a handicapped child); organs could be taken from people and 'redistributed' to those who most need them, even if this requires force or kills the 'donors'; 'confidential' information could be broadly shared; elderly, severely handicapped, permanently unconscious, expensive, terminally ill, and chronic patients could be abandoned, even killed; healthworkers might be forbidden to treat patients, including their own nearest and dearest, except in strict accord with the rationing scheme. Radical changes in the ethos of the health professions, programmes and institutions would be required: healthworkers would have to be discouraged from throwing themselves too readily into treating 'the patient in front of them'; tooth capping might have to be given priority over appendicectomies (as the Oregon poll suggested); and the like. Yet all these conclusions are so counter-intuitive that it is unlikely that even the proponents of QALYs would defend them; their failure to do so highlights the unsatisfactory nature of the theory when applied to real healthcare practice.

The reason that conclusions such as these would strike most people as being immediately 'counter-intuitive' is not that they are true but surprising or that they are false because unlikely to maximize overall utility; what is wrong with these conclusions is that they require us to compromise some of our most fundamental values such as integrity and fairness, some of our cardinal precepts such as respect for human life, bodily integrity and autonomy, some of our crucial relationships such as that between healthworker and patient, and some of our most basic traditions of healthcare practice; above all, *justice* is at stake. Utilitarianism has responded to such challenges elsewhere by mutating in various ways. First, as we saw above, increasingly sophisticated accounts of benefit have appeared, purifying it of certain repugnant preferences, giving greater weight to an irreducible plurality of 'prudential' goods or 'needs', and so on. Some theorists have dispensed altogether with the mathematicizing aspirations of earlier utilitarianism; others respond with much more sophisticated preference functions. Secondly, 'rule utilitarians' have argued that increased happiness (especially as conceived in terms of diverse goods) is only possible through the observance of certain ethical principles which limit the pursuit of any one good at the point at which it is detrimental to any other or to the dignity of persons or to the good of society.

These new multi-good and multi-principled versions of utilitarianism highlight and themselves overcome some of the problems with simpler utilitarianisms (such as QALYS); but they commonly share with their predecessors some of the other difficulties raised here, such as the willingness to compromise some basic norms of common morality. We have already noted how aggregation of community preferences and views of quality of life will predictably duplicate and even magnify common prejudices, deeming non-essential those treatments which are most often required by vulnerable groups: e.g. psychiatric care,

care for the elderly, treatments for substance abuse and treatment for AIDS sufferers. Because of its focus on total or average benefits, utilitarianism, while not aiming to bring about or confirm such disadvantage, is 'blind' to it where it occurs. QALYs are especially 'biased' against the elderly, the handicapped, the chronically sick, the dying, and other already disadvantaged people, for these groups are less likely to gain as many QALYs from a treatment as others. One commentator has dubbed this 'double jeopardy': 'The first disaster leaves the patient with a poor quality of life and when he or she comes forward for help, along come QALYs and finish him or her off!'[17] Thus QALYs amount to distribution in the opposite direction to the principles of liberal-welfarism outlined above: 'instead of operating to the absolute benefit of the worst-off members of society, they operate to their absolute detriment. For the worst-off members are those with the poorest quality of life coupled with the poorest life expectancy.'[18]

8.7 Beyond simple justice: mercy and the Good Samaritan

Even if one were satisfied that a utilitarian calculus such as QALYs does not compromise strict justice, there are other values and norms which must also be considered. Utilitarian systems of healthcare allocation make little or no allowance for 'Good Samaritanism': 'wasting' resources on saving or otherwise assisting someone in need with whom one is immediately confronted, rather than carefully planning and applying one's resources in the most efficient way. We believe that it can be morally desirable to intervene to save life and health even where this is apparently inefficient or not required by justice narrowly defined.

The readiness to rescue and the character traits which go with it (sensitivity to the plight of others, sympathy and empathy, ready self-sacrifice, active mercy) serve the preservation of individuals, communities and the species, and so are worthy of cultivation. They support the goals of common participation in life, health and friendship which, as we shall argue in the following chapters, are reasonable goals and fundamental goods. The habitual disposition to rescue promotes quick, easy and (in general) reasonable decision-making in situations where one might otherwise be paralysed (and people die) as a result of attempting much more complex reasoning about allocation of resources. This is especially true for health professionals: there are good personal, moral, psychological and sociological reasons for encouraging them to be well-practised in rescuing quickly in emergencies.

Another reason for supporting acts of rescue is that they are a symbolic demonstration of society's values. Rescue efforts say something about both the victim and the rescuer. The Good Samaritan does no utilitarian calculus before helping the man mugged and left for dead; he does not first ask whether the victim is a worthy candidate for his assistance by reference to potential QALY gains or his social contribution. The parable elucidates certain values (such as spontaneous generosity, a willingness to intervene in crisis, equal concern and respect, the sanctity of life, concern for the vulnerable...) which a society rightly promotes through its institutions. Medical rescue, therefore, acts as a kind of Good Samaritan parable, teaching and confirming these values in the rescuers and the witnesses (society).

So there *are* values in doing the apparently inefficient. We have focussed upon two: justice and mercy. There can be others. Utilitarianism rarely attends to the reflexive and narrative aspects of moral choices: what they make of us and say about us.[19] But if a particular healthcare distribution is adopted, it will have implications beyond its effectiveness in achieving health outcomes: there will be an impact on the character of individuals and the community.[20] Were healthworkers to decide to abandon or even kill certain expensive-to-treat patients and turn the resources saved to some good social use such as health promotion, utility might thereby be maximized, the proposal be efficient in terms of health gain; but apart from the harm to the victims such choices would harm the person who made them and any community which encouraged or condoned them. A doctor's character (attitudes and dispositions, and thus likely future choices) will inevitably be very significantly shaped by such a decision, however noble the motivation; so will the character of his profession or society be, insofar as they are complicit in that choice or influenced by it.

8.8 Conclusion

Utilitarianism undoubtedly has its attractions – in healthcare allocation as elsewhere. It has a certain appeal to commonplace sentiments such as benevolence, and to commonsense imperatives such as beneficence; it seems to accommodate a greater measure of scientific objectivity and hard-nosed realism than the liberal-welfarists. Two major attempts have been made to apply the theory to healthcare allocation, the QALY model and the Oregon state healthcare rationing scheme. Both have combined utilitarian insights with various polling techniques, cost-effectiveness and cost-benefit accounting, and mathematical models, which promise to yield some clear directions on healthcare allocation issues.

But many problems have arisen for the attempt to apply utilitarianism. No single, clear criterion of benefit and harm, or loss and gain, issues from utilitarian approaches to healthcare; no valid basis for measuring and comparing situations, choices or policies in healthcare allocation has emerged, at least none which is rationally compelling. Attempts then to translate such doubtfully made judgments of states of affairs into action guides were found to be fraught with further difficulties, including the willingness to compromise fundamental values such as justice and mercy.

Despite the various objections we have raised to any thoroughgoing utilitarian approach to healthcare allocation questions, we recognize that such theories helpfully challenge us to consider effectiveness and efficiency in this area as elsewhere: costing procedures, randomized clinical trials, hospital-based and peer-based utilization reviews, and evaluations of causality, outcomes and risk are undoubtedly important here. There is a duty to use one's resources (and a stronger duty when steward of other people's resources) in ways which are efficacious with regard to the purposes of the project concerned and not wasteful given the opportunity costs involved. A first step in any attempt to allocate healthcare must surely be to identify and eliminate harmful, ineffective or manifestly wasteful procedures. Without a concern for efficiency, provision of healthcare can become seriously distorted, providing very expensive therapies yielding little or no benefit at the opportunity cost of many other social goods, and failing to encourage greater responsibility on the part of patients and healthworkers. Cost-effectiveness studies may highlight certain unexpected facts: that, for instance, much universal health promotion is very expensive for little marginal benefit whereas some even high-technology interventions can actually be more cost-effective; or that increased healthcare spending often yields no improvement in health services but only a greater bureaucracy; or that increased health services may yield no benefit in terms of health. But if studies of efficiency and cost effectiveness and the like do have their place, they can never *per se* be a criterion of healthcare allocation: for effectiveness and efficiency are both qualifications of the *means* to ends which must first be determined (bearing in mind, of course, the resources available). There is no point in being very efficient and cost-effective at doing the wrong thing.

Conclusion to Part II

Chapters 6 to 8 have identified a number of obstacles – in our view insurmountable ones – to principlist, liberal-welfarist, and utilitarian-economic answers to healthcare allocation questions. This is not to deny that each of these contemporary approaches emphasises something of importance: in the case of the 'principlists', the need to see allocation issues within an overall ethical framework; in the case of the welfare-liberals, the concern to ensure universal access to quality health services; and in the case of the utilitarians, the concern to achieve 'value for money' in healthcare spending. All three concerns will find their proper place in the approach we advocate in the following chapters. What has emerged as most clearly lacking in contemporary 'liberal' approaches has been an understanding of the flourishing and goods of the human person in community which provides the only adequate framework of moral understanding within which to locate the rôle of healthcare in human life. The following part of our Report provides a basic exposition of the key elements in this framework.

Part III

A Framework of Moral Understanding for Healthcare Allocation

In Part II we argued that both longstanding practice in the allocation of healthcare and contemporary approaches to it lacked a truly adequate moral framework for assessing the justice of distributional arrangements. The four recurrent issues on which these approaches were found to be inadequate were:

1   the understanding of the human good, within which to situate activities and duties such as healthcare;
2   the understanding of the human person, who is the subject of healthcare, and of the needs of the person;
3   the understanding of community and the common good, by which to assess the responsibilities of others, especially government, to provide healthcare; and
4   the understanding of healthcare itself, with its distinctive social rôle and the requirements internal to its practice which are necessary to sustain that rôle.

In this Part of our Report we aim to offer a more adequate understanding of each of these topics in order to provide a better basis for the moral evaluation of allocational arrangements. In doing so we will be drawing upon several classical and current strands of thought: the Hippocratic medical-ethical tradition, Judeo-Christian social and bioethical teaching (considered in some detail in chapter 15), the classical natural law tradition and its contemporary revival, traditional and contemporary 'virtue ethics', and the recent 'communitarian' critique of liberalism.

9

Towards a substantive conception of the human good

This chapter introduces some basic concepts fundamental to any adequate framework of moral understanding and indicates some of their implications for healthcare. Human flourishing (a term which generically identifies the goal of our living) is constituted by our sharing in an irreducible plurality of incommensurable *'basic goods'*, among them life and health. The *basic* character of these goods means they possess the kind of worth in virtue of which they are ultimate reasons for choice and action: neither life nor health are merely instrumental goods, valuable only in virtue of other 'goods' they enable us to achieve. The fact that life and health are two among a *plurality* of basic goods means that they can be more or less the focus of attention in the actual life-plans of individuals. They may be the focus of professional care in the lives of some, while needing to be at least respected and in some measure cherished by everyone. *Positive moral norms* are intended to promote sharing in the basic goods; *negative moral norms* are intended to protect that sharing (by oneself or others) from choices which damage or impede it, and which therefore damage or impede human flourishing. Beyond moral norms, human beings need a range of virtues, that is dispositions readily to choose and act in ways which foster one's own and others' flourishing. The chapter specifies some of the norms and virtues important to the promotion and protection of life and health and the distribution of healthcare.

9.1 The notion of the good(s)

When we act, if we are acting humanly (freely and rationally), we do what we do – and refrain from doing other things – with some *goal* in mind: we hope to achieve something, to bring about some state of affairs, to obtain some kind of benefit, through or in the action. Why, for instance, does someone go to the doctor? Generally speaking: in order 'to 'get better'. The act of going to the doctor, the things doctors do, and the things we do or submit to on their advice, are largely to be explained by our desire for *life and health*, to which such activities are ultimately directed, whether self-consciously or only implicitly. Such ultimate goals behind our choices have been called *basic goods*. Others include friendship, knowledge, the exercise of skill in work and play, practical reasonableness and a right relationship to God. These goods make what we do intelligible; they are self-evident goals of human choice and fundamental to rational deliberation; they are aspects of human flourishing or happiness; and they are irreducible to other goods or ends.[1] We do not choose what these basic goods will be, even if we adopt our own personal hierarchies among them (what *I* think is the more important, what *I* will give most of my attention to); rather, our choices themselves presume and always seek our participation in one or more of these goods whether we realise it or not; the goods themselves are 'given' in our very nature and in the very nature of our choosing rationally.

9.2 Life and health as basic goods

Life and health, then, are basic human goods. Some people say, however, that life is only 'worth living', and health is only 'worth having', because of the *things they enable* – those conscious experiences, achievements and relationships which make life seem 'worthwhile' to us; when life and health fail to serve these other, more important ends, they are no longer valuable. If this is true then life and health are not truly basic goods: they are merely instrumental to some more important goods (such as certain conscious experiences). Life and health are often sought as means to such other goals; but it is also true that they are sought and enjoyed 'for their own sake'. That is why no-one expects us to give reasons for promoting life and health, avoiding sickness and death: we regard life and health as sufficient reasons *in themselves*, as *intrinsically* valuable. That is also why human life is said to be 'inviolable' and 'precious', to have a 'dignity' which surpasses the uses we make of it.

People can be *more* or *less* healthy. The enjoyment of well-ordered organic functioning in the life of a person whose faculties are fully developed is clearly different from the experience of health in the life of someone who is underdeveloped, or from the experience of someone who, because of impairment, enjoys only an approximation to well-ordered organic functioning. Some human beings suffer such severe and extensive damage as to seem to have lost the capacity for well-ordered organic functioning. Nonetheless, just because they are alive they are to be respected as human beings. If we think of the life of a human being as valuable only in so far as it is the *means* to achieving what we deem worthwhile we lapse into a dualism about human life which we shall criticise in chapter 10.

To say that life and health are basic goods does not of course mean that their prolongation, maintenance and/or improvement should be pursued by everybody, all the time, in all circumstances, at any cost, and by every possible means – far from it. Life and health are *not* the only or even the most important values: there are, as we have seen, other basic goods, and these are just as important. Different individuals adopt various hierachies of values in their various actions, commitments and choices of vocation and the pursuit of life and health will not necessarily feature as their first priority. A single-minded devotion to life and health would be irrational given the range of goods which are basic to human fulfilment. Nonetheless, the good of life is an obvious prerequisite for attaining other basic goods. And without the good of health – of well-ordered organic functioning – our faculties are often not exercisable in the measure we require to attain some of the other basic goods. Any rational plan of life would make prudent provision, therefore, for those things necessary for life and health: to ignore them altogether while pursuing some other goal would in most circumstances be irrational and as such immoral.

Some people will go further and, in keeping with their particular gifts, tastes, circumstances and sense of 'calling', commit themselves to a particularly healthy life-style or to the study and life-long practice of health promotion, medicine or nursing: in doing so they are placing life and health high among their priorities. (We should note that a commitment to healthcare will also obviously require a commitment to the good of *truth* and to the good of *skill in work*.) Any such commitment will structure a large part of a person's life, consume a great deal of his or her time and energy, and limit the pursuit of other goods such as play. Other people will focus their attentions elsewhere, perhaps risking or 'sacrificing' some of their potential life or health, accepting this loss as an undesired effect of their particular pursuit of skill, justice, religion or whatever. Neither choice of lifecourse would be unreasonable: as well as healthworkers there will naturally be mountaineers, soldiers and missionaries.

Without some such account of the value of life and health for people, healthcare is reduced to just one preference among many chosen as a matter of private whimsy or cultural conditioning rather than a rational pursuit within reasonable limits; if it is so viewed there is no basis upon which to assess what level and kind of healthcare is reasonably to be pursued and, as we shall consider below, reasonably to be expected from others. We shall consider in the next chapter the nature of the human person and the needs of persons; at this point, however, we might note that without some clear conception of the good it is far from evident why human needs should matter; they would enter into the description of the characteristics of rational animals but tell us nothing of any normative significance.

9.3 Why needs matter

We shall postpone to chapter 10 our consideration of the precise nature of human needs. But it is worth noting here that when people speak of 'needs' they usually mean to convey more than neutral information. When what is at stake are goods as basic as life and health we tend to treat those things necessary to their maintenance or improvement with particular seriousness. But why? One reason is anthropological, the other logical. First, while 'autonomy' or 'free will' is essentially a matter of our ability to fashion and refashion ourselves morally (and so, emotionally and intellectually) through our choices, there are undoubtedly certain logical and natural limits to self-creative choice. Needs are among these boundaries because we ignore them at our peril; they mark the points at which our choices or our negligence may harm, even extinguish, us, or at least disable us from pursuing our commitments and particular choices.

Secondly, as requirements for participation in particular basic goods and so for an aspect of human flourishing, needs are justificatory reasons for action which require no further justification; the pursuit of the satisfaction of needs, like participation in basic goods, is self-evidently valuable. Because the satisfaction of certain needs is a prerequisite to discharging other duties – whatever they might be – it is also a *prima facie* duty.

9.4 Moral norms

Our own personal preferences among the goods and our commitments will obviously have implications for our choices. But certain specific moral norms or guidelines will be required if we are to judge which ways are reasonable ways of pursuing these. If the fundamental and overarching requirement of our life is to 'do good and avoid evil', the existence of the various basic goods leads to the specification, in a number of norms, of what is involved in that fundamental requirement. Some will be positive ones, directing us to behave in certain ways, such as 'respect the dignity and equality of others', 'follow the Golden Rule' ('Do unto others as you would have them do to you'), 'preserve life', 'look after your health', 'help those in need', 'foster the common good', 'redistribute surplus wealth' and 'use efficient means'. Other norms are negative, forbidding us to act in certain ways, such as 'Do not intentionally kill the innocent', 'Do not deliberately harm', 'Do not abandon those in your care' and 'Do not lie'. These positive and negative norms make up the bulk of what has been described as 'commonsense morality' or 'common' morality.

Such moral norms will have particular applications to the situations and relationships specific to healthcare. Amongst the principles recognized in the Hippocratic tradition have been positive norms such as: 'act always for the benefit of the sick', 'deal justly and honestly with the patient' and 'respect professional confidences'; and negative norms such as 'never kill or assist the killing of a patient', 'never deliberately harm or take undue risks with a patient's health' and 'never abuse a patient sexually' – a code which is as relevant today as it was in the past even if it is by no means exhaustive.

Sometimes in medical or nursing care, as elsewhere in life, one is confronted with an immoral option which has its attractions. For example: one way of aiming for 'efficiency' in allocating healthcare resources would be to deny them to all severely handicapped, unproductive and elderly people. Such a choice would, however, amount to the abandonment of moral reason or to collusion between reason and prejudice or selfishness – hence the importance of moral norms such as the Golden Rule for sound reasoning and good living. At other times people have good objects but adopt immoral means to them – means which violate some basic good which is integral to the flourishing of persons. Since respect for persons requires respect for the whole range of goods constitutive of the flourishing of persons, we ensure that respect through observing certain norms: 'never act to destroy, damage or impede a basic good (i.e. a basic feature of human well-being)'; 'never treat a person as a means only but always as an end'; 'evil may not be done that good may follow'. These norms are the basis of inviolable human rights.

9.5 Moral virtues

Virtues are character traits which harmonize our feelings, intuitions, judgments, choices and actions with the pursuit of the good. They are essential to a well-lived life because they dispose us to want to do the right thing; they direct appropriately those feelings which contribute to moral perception of situations; they enable people to make good decisions quickly and to follow them through, without having to deliberate at length, always and at every moment, on what to do next; and they assist the identification of those options which best fit the agent's particular personality, situation, purposes, commitments and plan of life. Moral norms give direction to moral virtues, and moral virtues alert our perception to the applicability of moral norms.

Virtues which have an important bearing on the allocation of medical care include: *respectfulness* and *fellow-feeling*, which ensure an inclination always to treat one's patients as one's moral equals and to seek their good, especially their life, good health and comfort; *practical wisdom*, which enables quick, responsible decisions (e.g. about treatment); *courage and patience*, which include coming to terms with limitations of life-span, health, technology and circumstances; *moderation*, which includes resisting excesses in one's life-style which threaten one's good health and limiting one's expectations and demands of the health system to genuine needs; *justice*, which will make one fair and concerned for the common good in healthcare allocations as elsewhere; *mercy*, which looks beyond strict rights and duties and responds out of generosity and compassion to present 'crying need'; *fidelity* and *gratitude* towards those with whom one has a special relationship of care, such as one's own family, the elderly or patients; *truthfulness* which, without being insensitive or cynical, tells patients the facts (e.g. about the basis of healthcare allocations) and critically examines practices in this area; and *efficiency* which disposes one not to waste opportunities but to seek the most efficient and effective ways to achieving reasonable purposes.[2] Such virtues among healthworkers, patients and the general population are crucial to limiting demand for public medicine and ensuring its best distribution.[3]

Vices are the opposites of virtues: they organize various aspects of the human personality contrary to the pursuit of the good, so that the agent is torn between a will toward true flourishing and desires for mere fragments of it. Vices which might adversely affect the allocation of healthcare include: *partiality* (actively preferring patients of a particular race, age-group, social class...); *maleficence, infidelity* and *impiety* which incline people to harm or neglect patients; *meanness* on the one hand and *wastefulness* on the other; *imprudence* and *indecision*, which dispose one to act inappropriately if at all, e.g. regarding treatments and health systems; *cowardice*, which includes unreasonable fear of sickness, disability, healthcare or death or, in the face of sickness and care, assumes the posture of victim and passive recipient; and *intemperateness*, which allows passion or impulse to govern the agent as he or she lives an intemperate life-style or immoderately pursues various pleasures, the perfect body, independence, profit or all that is technologically possible.

9.6 Conclusion

In this chapter we have begun to introduce some of the fundamentals of the moral framework needed for understanding what is at issue in healthcare allocation: basic goods, moral norms and moral virtues. Healthcare is important to human flourishing. Our flourishing as human beings involves our successful sharing in a range of basic goods, including the good of life and the good of health. If we are to thus flourish we need to heed both the positive norms which guide our active sharing in basic goods and the negative norms which protect us from choices which subvert both our sharing and our capacity to share in those goods. If we are to be well-disposed to choose and act rationally in this regard we need a range of virtues.

Health is a basic good. Choices made and actions taken to promote health need to be consistent with respect for other dimensions of human flourishing involving other basic goods.

10

Persons and their needs

This chapter is principally concerned with defining some of the broad implications of the need human persons have for healthcare. It is because human personal existence is a *bodily* existence that bodily life and health (i.e. well-ordered organic functioning) are integral to our flourishing as human persons. What is integral to our flourishing gives rise to *basic needs*. We have basic needs for things necessary to bodily life and health, including a basic need for *healthcare*. Our need in this respect is a *recurrent* need for *appropriate* healthcare. Not all that passes for 'healthcare' is appropriate to meeting genuine human need. In particular, some 'healthcare' is designed to satisfy *desires* for things which are not necessary for life and health or even contrary to those goods. Genuine healthcare needs give rise to '*prima facie*' *duties* to make provision to meet the need, but provision should be made only in morally acceptable ways, and the capacity to make it may be significantly and sometimes entirely curtailed by circumstances. The chapter ends by considering the responsibilities *individuals* have for their own health.

10.1 Human beings are embodied

In the previous chapter we noted that were one to reduce life and health to merely instrumental goods one would be embracing a kind of dualism: what does this mean? People are *rational* animals but we are *animals* all the same: we are living beings or organisms and not simply minds or ghosts who happen to inhabit or use a body as dualists claim. We are all some*body*. If we are asked to identify someone, we are likely to point to a particular living bodily presence, and to describe what the person *looks like*. If someone strikes us or kisses us – whatever they do to our bodies – they do it to us. Bodily sensations, perceptions, emotions, afflictions (such as illness), activities (from movement to child-bearing) are integral to our lives as persons. So our bodies are *not* extrinsic instruments, like costumes or prisons or communication devices for some internal 'real me'. They enter into the constitution of the kind of being we are, they give us our concreteness, and they express or reveal us to others. Our mode of existence is bodily, and it is the organic, bodily aspect of human beings which makes life and health basic goods which are integral to our fulfilment as persons. If a person is healthy, health is an aspect of that person's well-being, not merely an attribute which is useful in achieving well-being.

To say that we are bodily beings is not to say that our lives should be understood in mechanistic or reductionist terms. On the contrary, the unity of the kind of bodily life we enjoy – a kind of life which is manifested in intellectual and spiritual activities, as well as physical and emotional ones – is only intelligible in virtue of a spiritual principle (called the rational soul). It remains that all human life as we know it is embodied; we are, and, as Christians, believe that after the resurrection we will be, bodily creatures. And if we are bodily beings then the good of our bodies, our life and health, is fundamental to being human.

A living human being remains a person deserving of respect even when his or her life is gravely impaired because of organic damage. A human being's inability to engage in the activities distinctive of human beings does not mean that human being is not a person. For a human person just is a living human being.[1]

10.2 Human beings have needs and healthcare is one

If organic life and health are goods of human beings certain things will be necessary if they are to enjoy them. When we say that someone *needs* something, we mean (at least) that in order to achieve their purposes that thing is required. The needed thing is both instrumental and necessary for the person to participate in some basic good; it is not a need if it does not truly serve the end of the agent attaining some good (it is no benefit to them) or if it is not necessary for that end (some other strategy can equally or better achieve it). Needs are called *basic* when they refer to those things 'we cannot get by without': things which are 'indispensable', 'fundamental', 'unforgoable' if the human person is to survive and flourish. Thus life-and-health needs are those things genuinely necessary if one is to enjoy the goods of life and health: things such as (nutritious) food, (clean) water, (adequate) clothing and shelter, (appropriate) exercise, rest and sanitation – and healthcare. If we are to participate in the goods of life and health at all (or at least for very long) and to flourish, we need healthcare broadly understood; this is especially true when we are sick or disabled; without medical and nursing care, especially in this situation, a person will be harmed. *Healthcare is a basic need of human persons.*

Life and health are themselves *also* instrumental to the achievement of the other basic goods. They 'put a human being in good shape for self-determination'; one has to be alive to enjoy life, and bodily health is necessary for the development and exercise of many abilities.[2] Thus life and health are required for the achievement of other basic goods; and so healthcare, as necessary for life and health, is in turn a need for participation in those other goods. Lacking access to medical care (or any of the other conditions for life and health) can thus be said to be doubly harmful: it endangers life and health (which are fundamental aspects of flourishing); and it endangers all other goods and choices which depend upon long life and good health. Healthcare, then, is both instrumental and necessary to participation in life and health, and through them to participation in all other goods, and something without which one is harmed (because hindered from flourishing).

On the face of it healthcare may seem a strange 'basic need' since demand for it differs so radically between persons, depending upon size, stage in life, disease and other factors. But this is true of most needs: bigger people need more food than smaller people; blind people need a different kind of education to sighted people; and so on. The need for healthcare, then, is not a need for healthcare in some unqualified sense of the term: it is a need for *appropriate* healthcare, i.e. self-care, medical and nursing services of the quality, quantity, and at the times, that well serve the life and health of a particular person. (This has obvious implications for the distribution of healthcare according to need: it cannot be egalitarian in a strictly mathematical sense.)

Another reason why healthcare can seem a strange basic need of all persons is that healthy people – which is most people most of the time

– might be thought not to *need* it. But the need for medical care, like the need for food, is recurrent; it cannot be satisfied 'once and for all' but must be provided for again and again. Thus even if a person is healthy and is said not to need healthcare 'at the moment' he or she is very likely to need it at some future point. Healthcare is what has been termed a 'course-of-life need', i.e. one which practically all people have *at some stage* of their lives. Furthermore, even when we are healthy we enjoy the benefits of preventive medicine of various sorts and we have a continuing 'security' interest in the ready availability of crisis healthcare.

10.3 Not everything that goes by the name of healthcare satisfies a need

Not all that goes by the name of 'healthcare' satisfies need. One commentator has suggested that 10% of medical care damages people's health, 10% has no effect on health, and 80% improves health – yet little is known with confidence about which therapies lie where.[3] Few people realize how few medical interventions have a solid scientific basis,[4] and how widely physicians diverge regarding the appropriate treatment for many conditions. Medical care is still relatively insignificant in the promotion of health,[5] though it has helped to ensure that a higher proportion of people approach or even exceed what is thought of as a natural life-span and that they do so in greater comfort.[6] Nor is increased spending on health services necessarily going to yield health improvements: it could, for instance, merely lead to increased provider incomes or increased bureaucracy.

We may desire things we do not really need; and we may need things we do not desire. Needs and desires differ in several important respects. First, whereas needs are *instrumental* and *necessary* to participation in basic goods, desires may well contribute nothing to participation in a basic good (they may simply seek satisfaction of feeling) or they may well be an unnecessary means to such participation. Secondly, whereas failing to satisfy a need risks harm to the agent, failure to satisfy a desire may represent no real harm and may even be of some benefit to the person. Thirdly, the harm, if any, in the absence of something desired depends upon whether the agent is conscious of the absence and counts it a loss, whereas the lack of something needed is a loss whether or not the agent knows or cares. Finally, people are in general aware of what they desire, but they can be – and often are – mistaken or ignorant about their real needs. Many a desire or preference is imagined or felt to be a need when it is in fact unhelpful, even harmful; people often entertain all sorts of 'false needs' and may well be encouraged to do so by individuals or forces around them, such as modern advertising which creates mythologies about the benefits and unforgoability of certain products.

The distinction between desires and needs is a crucial one for healthcare allocation. In highly medicalized societies it is commonly asserted that all possible medical treatment is a need. But as we have noted this is not the case: some is harmful, some ineffective or doubtfully effective; such care is, then, only a desire (at most), whether on the part of the patient or the healthworker. Furthermore, it is often asserted that we need 'the best available' or the latest or most fashionable or more expensive healthcare or that a condition of illness, disability or pain establishes a need for 'the best' treatment. But healthcare need only refers to what is instrumental *and necessary*, i.e. to that without which the goods of life or health are endangered. On this account many so-called health needs are more appropriately classified as mere desires. Commonly cited examples include:

- *cosmetic* as opposed to genuinely corrective treatments, such as much, though not all, cosmetic surgery, baldness therapies, tattoo removal, breast enlargement, buttock lift;
- *amenities* such as hotel-style hospital accommodation;
- *superhealth* promotion such as blood-doping for athletes or genetic research into improving human intelligence;
- *futile* treatments such as many complex surgical, mechanical, drug or other interventions for the incurable or dying;
- *doubtfully* effective treatments such as some traditional, fashionable and 'alternative' medicine; and
- *personal preferences* or 'socially-indicated' procedures such as contraception, sterilization, abortion, IVF, sex selection of children, sex-change operations and euthanasia.

If there is a case to be made for any of these procedures it is not in terms of healthcare need proper. Some 'healthcare' which does not serve health need might in fact serve some other need; more often it will serve some rational or irrational desire. Whether or not social provision in such situations is appropriate is another matter, and one to which we shall return. But insofar as these treatments satisfy desires which are not needs they will have a lower priority in the commitments of reasonable individuals and communities than genuine basic needs.

10.4 Needs are the basis of *prima facie* but not absolute duties

It is commonly asserted that the term 'need', properly used, is 'normatively strong' or 'persuasive': the identification of the need is itself a moral claim. Thus when international aid agencies, charities or interest groups announce that some group is in dire need, this is presumed to carry moral force. In these situations needs language not only describes things without which persons will, as a matter of fact, be seriously harmed or describes reasons why they or others may choose to act; it implies that those individuals *should* seek those needed things and others *should* help or at least not hinder them in this: *unless there were some serious counter-reason, it would not be rational for agents not to seek to satisfy the need.*

We say advisedly: 'unless there is some serious counter-reason', for healthcare needs do *not* create absolute duties. Someone might be told they 'need' a certain medical procedure. Depending upon his reasonable personal priorities, responsibilities and opportunities, his estimate of the risks and probable effectiveness of the various available courses of action, and the various counter-arguments which might be mustered, he may assess the force of this claim in a variety of ways. He may, for instance, reasonably judge that the proposed procedure would be disproportionately burdensome in terms of the pain, physical side-effects, disruption, confinement, embarrassment, risk and cost consequent on it and so decide to forgo it.[7] Or he may judge the procedure incompatible with his other serious purposes and determine that it is worth 'taking the risk' of not pursuing the proposed treatment. Harmonizing one's healthcare choices with other elements of one's plan of life could never mean neglecting life and health entirely, but it will likely require moderating healthcare demands. It would rarely be reasonable, for instance, to impoverish one's own family to the point of starvation just so as to extend one's own already long life, and it may be noble to forgo certain healthcare opportunities for the sake of others. On the other hand, one's responsibilities (e.g. to young dependants) may generate an additional responsibility to care for one's own health. Thus however important the concept of need is to the issue of healthcare allocation and other matters, it is not some kind of 'trump' which ends all further ethical discussion or discernment. Needs are *non-conclusive reasons for action* and found *non-absolute duties*.

Likewise not all ways of satisfying a need will be morally warranted. Some means will be forbidden by moral norms, e.g. obtaining a kidney for transplant by kidnapping someone and stealing it from them. Other proposals may be unreasonable because inefficient (e.g. putting all patients on intensive care) or disproportionate in terms of side-effects (e.g. amputating when a course of drugs would have saved the diseased limb) or inappropriate in the particular circumstances (e.g. during a time of severe shortage). Yet others may be motivated by excessive fear of sickness and unwillingness to accept the inevitability of death, or by pride and vanity in the search for the perfect body, or by infatuation with the technologically possible, or by a selfish lack of concern for the needs and claims of others. The satisfaction of needs is subject to various moral norms: we indeed must seek what we need, *but only in morally reasonable ways*.

10.5 Individuals should attend to their own needs

In the next section we shall consider the duties of others to assist with healthcare. But responsibility for healthcare clearly begins with the individual's stewardship of his own health. The duty to use reasonable means to provide for one's own health needs can be spelt out as a range of duties:

- we should seek relevant information about healthy living, avoidance of and responses to ill-health;
- we should act reasonably on this information so as to minimize illness and injury, developing virtues of moderation and avoiding behaviour which threatens our health (e.g. work patterns, fashions, certain types of sexual behaviour);
- we should seek to cooperate with health professionals and others to deal with medical problems as they arise and to anticipate and prevent them insofar as possible;
- we should attend to our healthcare needs appropriately and in order of importance.

It is obvious that not all needs are equal: some are greater, more urgent or more serious than others. In our next chapter we shall examine how needs might be ranked. But at this point it is worth noting that this will have implications for the normativity of needs. If needs can sometimes be ranked as greater and less, then the seriousness of the duty to seek to satisfy them will, *ceteris paribus*, vary accordingly. One will have *more* reason to seek to fulfil more urgent or more crucial health needs than less urgent or less crucial ones; and the more urgent or crucial the need, the graver must be any counter-reason for not seeking to meet it.

In summary, then, we can say that the duty to satisfy one's needs, and to satisfy them in order of importance, must be qualified by practicalities, proper commitments, and right reason. Nonetheless there is a *prima facie* duty. Any consistent failure to seek to attend to healthcare needs, or subordination of them to the satisfaction of unnecessary preferences, should be questioned, as it could represent an irrational devaluation of life and health, a direct (and so immoral) act against those basic goods, or an exaggeration of the importance of some other good at the expense of all others.

11

The nature of human community and the provision of healthcare

This chapter is concerned with the relationship between human beings and human communities as the moral foundation of duties to meet the healthcare needs of others. The conception of community we present is radically opposed to atomistic views of human association. All of us are profoundly dependent on relationships of cooperation for our existence and the possibilities of flourishing as human beings. Hence the important truth that to promote the common good of the community is to promote one's own good.[1] Since cooperative relationships are a moral necessity they give rise to duties to sustain and create the conditions of flourishing which should exist at different levels of community. These general truths are exemplified in the character of the duties to provide healthcare proper to different levels of community.

The most fundamental level of community is the family. The family has duties of healthcare precisely because of the character of the commitment to faithful love between spouses and for children proper to a family founded on the marriage relationship. But these duties are limited by a family's resources and other serious commitments. Sophisticated and expensive healthcare can be made available only through a higher level of social organization. Hence the provision of healthcare is an important feature of the common good of societies, i.e. one of those conditions of human flourishing which complex levels of social cooperation exist to serve.

Because every human being has a claim to flourish, the social resources of healthcare should be distributed justly, which in the first place means *fairly* in relation to need. The requirements of justice in distributing resources may be expressed in terms of rights and duties. Societies do not have to arrive at uniform solutions to the problem of providing healthcare in order adequately to recognise the right to it. One kind of solution rather than another will be imposed by a society's distinctive tradition and culture, and a range of such solutions may satisfy the requirements of justice. The chapter ends by clarifying one extremely important type of constraint on distributional arrangements. Healthcare practice properly understood should be informed by respect for moral values, observance of moral norms, and the practice of the relevant virtues. Arrangements for healthcare provision which have the effect of undermining the character of the moral commitment of doctors and nurses are contrary to the interests of all, especially patients.

11.1 The need for a substantive conception of community

If persons have, generally speaking, duties to attend to their own healthcare needs by reasonable means, do others have a duty to co-operate in satisfying these needs, and if so, to what extent? What is it reasonable to expect from the members of the communities in which one lives? Is there a right to healthcare, and if so to how much?

Most people belong to several communities, such as those of the nuclear and extended family, of the neighbourhood, of the workplace, of town and of nation. Each involves a sharing of life and purposes supported by nature, mutual expectations, customs, and formal or informal agreements. The more the parties involved are joined by 'affective' bonds (of blood, friendship, piety, loyalty, patriotism, gratitude...), have common interests and goals, engage in joint projects and activities, the more common life they share. Basic goods provide reasons for action by a person even when such action is with a view to another's benefit or their joint benefit. Norms requiring impartiality and service of the common good, and associated virtues, commend action with a view to serving the good of others, including their life and health.

A 'communitarian' or 'social' consciousness runs contrary to that asocial 'individualism' many see implicit in 'liberal' conceptions of the person, the community and the good examined in Part II. On these liberal accounts, people's highest-order interest is in 'getting their own way' (achieved through the exercise of 'autonomy', the capacity to frame, revise and pursue one's own, privately chosen preferences or conceptions of the good, whatever these might be) and society is a loose conglomeration of individuals each pursuing his or her private interests either in competition or for certain mutual benefits. Several commentators have noted the power of such 'individualism' in medical practice, especially in America, but even here in Britain the change in social temper and ideology in the last two decades of the twentieth century has meant a move towards a more 'privatised' view of people's interests and relations, in healthcare as elsewhere.

We would argue, however, that relationships and co-operation of various sorts are essential not only to the achievement of many purposes and thus to self-realization: they are also in part constitutive of the very self which is realized and fulfilled. People's sense of identity, commitments and personal values to a large extent come with their ties to family, work-place, village or neighbourhood, class, party, church, club, nation and so on. With this range of attachments comes a variety of debts, inheritances, expectations and obligations which constitute the 'given' of life, its 'moral starting point', and give it much of its 'moral particularity'. People's goals and commitments are also unavoidably interrelated. Basic goods such as life and health, for instance, we come to have in virtue of relationships; knowledge of the truth we acquire in virtue of the intellectual labour of past generations and our participation in institutions of learning; a good such as friendship is essentially social; these and others are in some degree necessary to human flourishing. Even in the most 'liberal' and atomised society, certain basic goods, needs, relationships and responsibilities will remain fundamental to human nature and choice, and to the very possibility of community itself. And on this natural commonality will be built various shared understandings through which members of a community come reasonably to expect mutual assistance especially in meeting crucial needs.

Yet another reason supporting a richer conception of community than that proposed by the theories examined in Part II is that the diverse commitments of individuals are much *influenced* by those of others. No one simply decides 'out of the blue' to become a health professional: people do so because they see and are attracted by this practice in action and perhaps by certain 'icons' of it; and they do so by joining a group and a tradition with 'its own ways'. Institutions such as hospitals, the National Health Service, the medical Royal Colleges and the Royal College of Nursing are bearers of traditions which partly constitute the common life of their members by a continuous (and evolving) 'argument' as to what a good health system, hospital, medical or nursing practice might be.[2] People are also subordinate characters in the life-stories of others, such as their spouse, parents, children and work colleagues. Thus the settings for our own plans of life and particular choices and actions are limited and shaped in ways not entirely fixed by us but given by a prior history of other people's life-plans and choices, and by those responsibilities which result from our unchosen as well as chosen relationships.

Principles of justice and social institutions built on individualistic and adversarial conceptions of human relations may well serve only to promote such an orientation. But if one accepts that persons are related more profoundly and in morally more significant ways than individualistic liberal accounts allow, one will reject any simplistic claim that 'I am not my brother's keeper'. The *common humanitarian duty of care* includes both negative duties (not to harm, treat negligently or with disrespect) and positive ones (to rescue, help or otherwise show kindness to people where it would not require an unreasonable burden). Just how far duties to help others will extend depends on a variety of factors such as: how closely the parties are related (formally or in affection or in custom); what prior undertakings have been given or implied; whether the person in need of care can provide for him or herself; whether there are others with a greater responsibility to provide the care; and the agent's other resources, goals and responsibilities.

11.2 Healthcare begins at home

We have argued that the primary responsibility for healthcare is the individual's. This responsibility is commonly extended to the individual's family. The special kind of unity that the family founded on marriage has constitutes it as a special kind of community[3] – one of physical connection (through procreation, and therefore in genetic constitution, through physical and temperamental resemblances), of cultural bonds (by common experience, knowledge, language, views), and of commitment (devotion to finding part of one's self-fulfillment in helping the other members to flourish).[4]

Though families vary in their expectations, depending upon both natural circumstances and cultural mores, yet individuals and societies – from the richest to the poorest, the most 'primitive' to the most 'advanced' – will almost always rely upon the family as the first provider of needs as basic as healthcare.

The family is the first community of healthcare because it is the family members who (normally) feel and accept as their natural responsibility the care of the other members of the unit. Families quite naturally engage in all sorts of health-related activities, supporting the pregnant mother, feeding and washing the children, applying plasters to wounded knees, caring for the one in bed with the 'flu, calling the doctor, paying the medical bills (where necessary), and so on. We regard it as a mark of the functional family that it provides its members with various things which are indispensable to the pursuit of good health and long life: security and consolation in illness; sensitivity to each other's state of health and basic needs; communication of inherited wisdom and personal experience of basic principles of self-care (safety, diet, hygiene, medicine, the warning signals as to when to seek care from others and so on); and a willingness and ability to sacrifice much in the way of time, care and resources to ensure the good health of the members.

As with the duty of the individual to care for his own health, so that of the family to care for its members' health is not absolute. Families have no responsibility to spend all their energies and resources on keeping each other alive and healthy: they properly have other goals as well. But family healthcare is a very special instance of the 'common humanitarian duty of care' described above. Thus while the common law recognizes no general duty to intervene as a Good Samaritan and help another (even if morality to some extent does), it nonetheless holds that those who by nature or choice have assumed the care of others do have a greater responsibility to provide such positive care.[5] Familial provision of healthcare is thus an expression of friendship and affection, a communal pursuit of goods such as life and health, and a response to natural or chosen duties of care supported by social institutions such as law.

11.3 Healthcare is also a social good

Life and health, we have argued, are goods common to members of any community, and these are pursued through various collaborative ventures including the provision of healthcare. They are also part of 'the common good' of communities, for several reasons. First, joint action is usually the most efficient and effective way, and commonly enough the only way, of achieving these goods. Health and life are subject to (largely) undeserved, unpredictable, costly, and unevenly distributed dangers which few can adequately cover from their own resources alone. If it is a function of society to attempt to ensure the conditions of flourishing for all, then individuals and families will naturally look to others for assistance when they cannot themselves meet needs as fundamental as basic medical and nursing care.

Secondly, ill-health is sometimes contagious and thus a threat to the good of others or even of all. But even where it is not contagious it presents a threat to the community. The good health and long life of its members is usually a benefit to a community, and the ill-health or death a loss, to particular others in that community (dependants, loved ones, fellow-workers...) and to the community as a whole which suffers the loss of the activity and society of that member.

Thirdly, the disposition to act readily as the Good Samaritan did in response to need is one which there are good practical reasons for encouraging in health professionals and others – it helps them to deal well with emergencies, and to cooperate in the advance of medical care. The 'common humanitarian duty of care' (or the duty to be a 'Good Samaritan') is not only a conclusion of the understanding of morality expounded here: it is embodied in documents ranging from the Bible and Koran to the International Covenant on Economic, Social and Cultural Rights, in many different theories of morality, religious and secular, and in many historical practices of our society including of course the establishment and support of the NHS. Acts of rescue are symbolic demonstrations of crucial social values, such as respect for the dignity and equality of persons. Thus there may be rather more to a health service than first meets the eye: for a health system functions not only as a mechanism for health improvement but as a stage on which are set and enacted important values of the community.

For all these reasons and others the provision of healthcare is part of the common good of any society, part of what society is for. This does not determine exactly how much healthcare, how provided and for whom, but it does run contrary to views, such as some examined in chapter 6, that the state must remain 'neutral' and uninvolved in such matters (see 6.2). Experience suggests that reliance upon the free market alone in healthcare will fail to satisfy those requirements of the common good just outlined (see 5.3). Most states have some historical experience of undertaking a substantial rôle as co-ordinator, regulator and provider of healthcare, even if some governments have been scaling down their involvement in recent years. Healthcare continues to be viewed as an 'essential service' similar to others which are nationalized or at the least heavily regulated and subsidized in most societies because public interest in their just and efficient provision is so great – services such as law and order, defence, education, energy, transport and communications.

11.4 Healthcare is a matter of distributive justice

Recognition of the fundamental dignity of every human being entails recognition of the claim of each to flourish as a human being. The end of political society is the fulfillment of all its members, including provision for their needs where the market or their own resources fail to satisfy. That being so, societies and their institutions have healthcare responsibilities similar to those of the individual and the family: to use reasonable means to attend to needs in order of importance; to set healthcare high among social goods; to moderate this provision according to appropriate norms and virtues, while bearing in mind other responsibilities of the state.

Since individuals in their relations with each other, both immediate and mediated through institutions, constitute society, they have obligations to favour and foster the common good of their communities, i.e. that set/ensemble of conditions which enables the members of a community to attain for themselves reasonable objectives through which they come to flourish as human beings. Societies are not to be viewed reductively as mechanisms for the pursuit of the interests of particular persons or groups: they should embody arrangements conducive to the good of all. Community membership should expand the range of possibilities for individuals pursuing basic goods such as life and health but it can also erect new obstacles to that pursuit. Various responsibilities will arise under law, public policy, private contract, debt, fellowship, family tie, custom, position of authority, and so forth; and responses to these, as well as to one's personal goals, will be shaped by the web of relationships in which one is involved and by the coinciding and conflicting hierarchies of values which others in those relationships have and pursue.

Distributive justice is that part of justice concerned with problems of distributing resources and opportunities which are essentially common but which for the sake of the common good must be appropriated to individuals.[6] For the reasons we outlined in chapter 5 (5.3.2) healthcare is just such a 'resource' or 'opportunity': for it is largely a co-operative enterprise, indeed a social creation – the product of accumulated knowledge and skills, publicly funded professional training, public hospitals, state accreditation and licensure and so on – and must be 'appropriated' to particular individuals if it is to occur at all.[7]

If healthcare *is* a distributable resource, the next question that arises is on what basis it should be distributed. Fundamental to communal morality are norms of impartiality and solidarity, especially the Golden Rule. This principle involves both a recognition that basic goods are to be shared by all human beings and an active but impartial concern for others, modelled on concern for self and those one loves. It includes respect for the dignity of others as persons, as one's moral equals, trust in them, a concern to avoid harming them or thwarting their legitimate interests, a desire in various ways to co-operate with and serve them, and to achieve as far as possible basic harmony with them. Applied to our present concerns the Golden Rule so understood might suggest the following tests: Would I think the healthcare budget and its distribution was fair if I (or someone I loved) were in healthcare need, especially if I were among the weakest in the community (i.e. sick with a chronic, disabling and expensive ailment, and poor and illiterate)? Would I think it were fair if I were one who would go without under the proposed arrangements? Would I think it fair were I a healthworker, healthplanner, taxpayer and/or insurer?[8] Answering these questions requires adopting a proper form of imaginative identification with the points of view of all others affected by the distribution in question. From this we can conclude that the primary basis for healthcare distribution will be need for healthcare where satisfaction of that need is compatible with the fulfilment of similar and more important needs of other members of that community.[9] And one of the functions of community provision of healthcare will be to act as a conduit from those who have more than they need to those who have less than they need.[10]

11.5 Different communities will give differing degrees of priority to healthcare

We have argued that 'efficiency within reason' is a requirement of morality: this is as true for societies as it is for individuals. Communities must seek to bring about good in the lives of their members by actions, institutions and programmes which are efficient for their reasonable purposes. So, for instance, where one medical care programme offers all the benefits of another plus more, the more beneficial programme is to be preferred other things being equal. Most often, however, there will be some benefits and burdens in one possible programme and some in another, and neither will be compellingly preferable. Incommensurability restricts the possible operation of cost-benefit analyses here as elsewhere in human choice. There is no compelling reason for thinking that health, for instance, is one and a half times as important as defence and is thus to be granted one and a half times as great a budget. Nor could a community rationally hold that truth must be compromised for the sake of health-maximization (by, for instance, deliberately exaggerating the 'dire' risks of certain activities in a health scare campaign), as if truth can somehow be weighed against health according to some common denominator. We need not rehearse here the logical and practical difficulties of any such consequentialist calculus: they have been treated in chapter 8 (see 8.5).

Are the choices communities make between, say, health and defence, or between the old and the young, or between preventative and acute care, purely arbitrary then – properly the product of happenstance, powerful interest groups and the horse-trading that is the stuff of ordinary politics? Or is there some more rational standard from which one might criticize the results of such a process?

We think there is. First, communities, like individuals, will face a range of morally *unreasonable* options. Communities and their leaders, like private individuals, must be fair, impartial, willing to help. Thus social policies will be excluded which involve intentionally killing or harming the innocent, unreasonable discrimination, punitive motivations, disrespect for conscience or autonomy, lying, and so on (see further chapter 14).

Secondly, amongst the range of *reasonable* options in areas such as healthcare allocation, a community will adopt one which is in keeping with its reasonable commitments linked to customs, traditions, shared values and various kinds of negotiation and consensus. These commitments will sometimes be formally expressed in constitutions, treaties, laws, policies, 'patient charters', established codes of professional conduct, and the like; at other times they will be manifested more informally in customs and more or less unquestioned expectations. Then some sorts of fairly rough and ready cost-benefit analysis of the various possible institutions and programmes might be possible and advantageous, sometimes yielding some determinate 'best solution' to a particular problem, at other times a range of more or less satisfactory solutions. So a community might reasonably ask: 'will this proposal contribute to the war effort?' and 'will this alternative contribute more to the war effort?' – though sometimes, of course, such questions will not make sense. But even a community not so strongly focused as one at war will be able to ask: 'are we satisfied with our level of defence spending?', 'could we not afford to spend more on care of the elderly?', 'does not the cutting of spending on mental health conflict with our avowed egalitarianism and concern for the disadvantaged?' and so on.

What we are suggesting here is that any society such as the UK shares a common if often hazy and ill-defined vision of what kind of a community it wants to be. Aspirations to being 'a safe society' and 'a caring society' have, for instance, often been articulated here by political leaders and others, and might be said to be manifest in various welfare programmes. Our health system may be thought to embody some commitment to the following values (though in some cases the commitment is manifestly defective to the point of subverting those values): the dignity and equality of persons, the sanctity of human life, the importance of health, special concern for the vulnerable and the suffering, respect for the elderly, the importance of family life, and the value of community. Such notions as we find them realised – however unfocussed or fuzzy or defective their embodiment might be – amount to culturally particular expressions of the principles of justice, establish standards of aspiration, criticism and debate, contribute to our self-understanding, and underpin many of our institutional arrangements. The radical difference between the universal healthcare system of the UK and the prevailing free market (supplemented by some government aid) in the US reflects deep ideological differences. But as long as neither is a necessarily unjust system (though it is clear that at present some aspects of both systems surely are unjust), it is fitting that each community will choose the system which better reflects its temper, history and enduring values.

11.6 Socio-cultural differences do not serve to call in question a right to healthcare

The language of 'rights', suitably underpinned by an adequate

understanding of justice, can be used to express many of the requirements of justice.[11] Rights are two-sided. From the perspective of the
right-holder they amount to claims about what he or she can reasonably expect (is 'due') from others by way of their acting and forbearing
to act; if a right remains unsatisfied, the right-holder is reasonably
aggrieved, has cause for complaint. From the perspective of the
duty-bearer, rights amount to claims about what he or she reasonably
owes to others by way of action and restraint. Both the right-holder
and the duty-bearer can be an individual, a group of particular individuals, a whole community or its representative institutions, but in each
case rights claims are claims about how people should, in justice, treat
each other.

Sometimes rights represent constraints on the behaviour of individuals and communities (e.g. the right not to be arbitrarily arrested):
such rights may be 'trumps' or have an absolute veto power, in that
they cannot morally be set aside even at the behest of majorities or
for what one might suppose to be the overall good of society. At
other times rights will have some degree of precedence over other
interests, but will not be absolute, e.g. the right to shelter. Insofar as
assistance from others in the provision of healthcare is reasonably
expected it is *prima facie* matter for this second kind of right. When
one talks of a right precisely what is at issue needs to be specified by
clarifying who the right-holders and duty-bearers are, what the
content of the right/duty is (in terms of unambiguous descriptions of
activities, including the times and other circumstances and conditions
for the applicability of the duty), and any conditions under which a
right/duty might be lost or waived.[12]

We have identified the holders of the right to healthcare as all
members of the community (both the presently sick and the potentially
sick), especially those with conditions which exceed their own capacity
(and that of their family) to help cure or satisfactorily mitigate, and the
bearers of the duty to provide healthcare as the individual (regarding
his own health), his family and near neighbours, the health professions, and the various communities of which the right-holder is a
member, up to the level of the state. We have clarified the content
of this right/duty as a duty to provide (and a right to expect) access
to appropriate healthcare but only insofar as this is consonant with
fulfilling certain negative duties (not to kill, harm, abandon, lie . . .
see chapter 14), certain positive duties (to respect, care, promote
health, observe the Golden Rule . . .), certain moderating virtues,
and certain individual and communal hierarchies of values; in chapters

12 and 13 we shall examine the specific allocation criteria designed to ensure access to healthcare consonant with these conditions and to help sort the claims of competing rights-holders.

By what standard are we to judge whether a particular community's present specification and demarcation of healthcare rights, as in its healthcare institutions and policies, are reasonable? Liberal protestations notwithstanding, one cannot avoid assessing these against some substantive understanding of the good of persons in community, some 'pattern' or range of 'patterns' of ideal human character, conduct, and interaction in community, while making appropriate provision for individual initiative and interaction and appropriate differences between traditions and cultures, as these will affect such a pattern.[13] Such a standard of criticism will hold in dialectic, as it were, the 'objective' standards of promoting individual flourishing in community proposed in the present chapter (including the claim that health is better than illness, and the objective of ensuring universal access to some decent minimum level of healthcare) while allowing plenty of scope for a range of reasonable but culturally or situationally specific solutions to the attainment of such goals. A society such as ours must, then, debate openly and freely its particular solutions to these problems, seeking to achieve some level of consensus or at least compromise within the range of reasonable options, settling the various competing claims by some appropriate and recognized decision-making process, and remaining open to renegotiation and revision.

Our account of the principles of justice in the allocation of healthcare requires a great deal of specification of healthcare entitlements by legislative and executive institutions formulating policy in the light not only of these principles but of the specific needs of their citizens, the availability of resources, and the practicalities of modern healthcare delivery. The need to ensure adequate provision for healthcare needs might warrant the establishment of some sort of positive (legal) rights for patients and of codes of conduct among the health professions which would include allocational principles. The positive rights of citizens to medical and nursing care might then be satisfied by a mixture of the market-place (through self-provision, fee-for-service and insurance schemes) and state provision through the NHS, and any decisions by the state to limit its involvement would be recognized as either a (more or less reasonable) reliance upon the free market to allocate or an abdication of responsibility in this area.

11.7 Towards a substantive conception of healthcare practice

Contemporary Western societies entrust to the medical and nursing professions much of the task of healthcare. They do so on the understanding that *professional* healthcare is a particular kind of calling and practice, with particular skills, approaches, ethics and ideals. Without such a background the authority of a profession would be unintelligible.[14] Notions such as 'vocation' and 'profession' are specifically ethical ones, and entail:

- a conviction about the importance of a particular service of others and one's 'suitedness' to it;
- preparation for and training in the practice and acceptance into the practice by fellow practitioners;
- some kind of implied or actual profession on the part of the professional that he or she freely undertakes continuing devotion to that way of life in active service of a high good which will call forth a certain devotion of character and life; and
- public recognition (accreditation, licensure, membership of a society, privileges and emoluments) that the professional is trained and competent to act in a particular way.[15]

All this requires a certain baseline of agreement, certain shared values which allow for cohesion amongst the members of the profession and for a kind of 'objectivity' or impersonality of judgment that transcends personal preference. It also founds those mutual expectations, duties, loyalties and norms which are the conditions of freedom to practice a particular 'art' and of public confidence in the practitioner.

Thus just as individuals and communities need norms, virtues and commitments in order to live in accord with moral wisdom, so do health professionals. Many norms applicable to healthcare which are the substance of 'bioethics' codes are translations to the healthcare situation of norms more generally applicable in human action. These include:

- duties to refrain from certain actions in dealings with patients, such as intentional killing, violence, non-consensual interference, manipulation, exploitation, neglect, abandonment, lying, breaches of confidentiality, and unjust discrimination;

- positive duties to act in certain ways with respect to patients, such as with equal respect, in keeping with the trust which should characterise the doctor-patient relationship, responsive to needs and their relative import, with reverence for life, with a view to saving, curing and caring, encouraging people to live responsible and healthy lives, giving special care to the most disadvantaged; and
- duties to act in certain ways with respect to fellow healthworkers and the community, e.g. stewarding common resources justly and efficiently.

Thus the Declaration of Geneva,[16] a modernized version of the Hippocratic Oath, requires physicians to consecrate their lives to the service of humanity; to make the patient's health their first concern; to prevent 'considerations of religion, nationality, race, party politics, or social standing coming between my duty and my patient'; to 'maintain utmost respect for human life from its beginning'; and not to use medical knowledge 'contrary to the laws of humanity'. Any reasonable plan for allocating healthcare, insofar as it involves healthworkers, will have to accommodate such norms.

The virtuous person does not simply observe certain moral norms: he or she is distinguished by having a certain kind of character. Likewise in healthcare: the good physician or nurse is not merely the one who obeys some ethical code but one with certain dispositions. While all of us need all of the virtues to live well certain dispositions have a particular importance in the life of a doctor or nurse: *Good Samaritanism* (which disposes one to do one's best to save, heal and care for others even at some self-sacrifice or apparent inefficiency); *courage* (which imports a willingness to confront the challenge represented by grave and perhaps seemingly incurable illness in others); and *justice* (which ensures that one is not self-seeking, prejudiced or evasive in the exercise of one's healthcare responsibilities but concerned always for one's particular patients and the common good). A persistent temptation for healthworkers, as indeed today for the community more generally, is to medicalize the whole of life and to create ultimately unfulfillable expectations. Thus one virtue of particular relevance to our present concerns is *practical wisdom*: applied to medicine, an understanding of what truly lies within the competence of doctors, and an ability to see not merely what is outside the province of medicine but also when medical treatment itself becomes futile. And in view of the grave problem for healthcare allocation of demand created by supply there is a need for *moderation*: for researchers, developers, marketers, health reporters and health-workers to act and speak with appropriate restraint.

Several recent writers have called for a re-emphasis on those values and virtues crucial to the practice of medicine which, if lost, will vitiate the traditional character of the doctor-patient relationship as a healing encounter or 'covenant'. They argue that beneficence towards one's particular patients, solidarity with all who suffer and concern for the common good are values more in keeping with the ethical roots of medicine than are autonomous individualism, profitability or econo-mistic efficiency (see chapters 7 and 8). On this view, consistent with that proposed in the present chapter, healthcare is about sustaining and enlarging the realisation of certain basic goods in the lives of persons in ways which make for the flourishing and well-being both of those who are cared for (patients) and those who care (nurses and doctors). Healthcare is not about fulfilment of preferences, or the maximization of measurable efficiency. Alternative proposals, such as a shift from patient-centred to procedure-driven medicine, or from Hippocratic to market ethics, would require a radical redrawing of medical practice as traditionally conceived and a similarly radical transformation of medical ethics – one which, on the account presented here, would be contrary to the good of persons and of the profession itself. And this means that health professionals must be ready and willing to take part in leadership and social criticism to help ensure that the health system or their own profession does not slide in undesirable directions.

Conclusion to Part III

In chapters 9 to 11 we have sought to correct deficiencies marking longstanding and contemporary approaches to the allocation of healthcare: impoverished conceptions of the human person, the human good, our common life and the nature of healthcare. We have done so by elaborating an account of the basic goods of human choice, the basic virtues of good character and the basic principles of action which are fundamental to ethics and true flourishing. These things make healthcare intelligible. Individuals have a *prima facie* responsibility to seek to satisfy their healthcare needs and to seek help from others where this is necessary. Examination of the concepts of community, the common good and distributive justice helps to establish the basis and extent of the duties of those others to assist. From the family to the society, various overlapping communities have responsibilities for the provision of healthcare, much of which is achieved through the health system. Core social values will also be expressed therein. Fundamental to sorting conflicting needs and rights claims will be the question: would I think the healthcare budget and its distribution were fair if I (or someone I loved) were to be in healthcare need, especially if I were to be among the weakest in the community (i.e. sick with a chronic, disabling and expensive ailment, poor and illiterate)? Properly understood there is a right to healthcare and communities have a duty to satisfy this right within the confines of what is morally reasonable and the particular opportunities and character of that community. The mores and virtues particular to the health professions will also have a bearing on what is appropriate in the provision of healthcare. The moral framework we have outlined in Part III allows us to examine the various allocation criteria which have been proposed for healthcare.

Part IV

Criteria and Considerations relevant to Allocation Decisions

Introduction to Part IV

In this part of the Report we shall review some of the criteria which are actually in use in the NHS or which have been proposed for use in the distribution of healthcare. We shall evaluate them in turn in the light of the moral framework expounded in Part III. It should be noted, however, that in any particular allocation decision more than one standard may be influential, without the influence always being fully articulated. Furthermore, even where a single standard seems to be straightforwardly applied, one or more others may still have some influence on choice. While in Chapters 12 and 13 we shall treat the criteria separately, we do not pretend that they are always employed in that way to the exclusion of other criteria. Indeed, some of our discussion will show that they cannot be.

Differing understandings of social justice are associated with the following different standards thought appropriate to healthcare allocation:

- to each equally;
- to each according to the free market;

- to each according to their social contribution;
- to each according to their merit or desert;
- to each according to their needs.[1]

In Chapter 12 we review at some length criteria which in themselves are an inadequate or erroneous basis for the allocation of healthcare. In Chapter 13 we explain the most important criterion for determining healthcare allocation – healthcare need. This criterion does not, however, represent the sole consideration which has to be borne in mind in allocation decisions. And so, in Chapter 14 we detail some of the other considerations which must to be borne in mind if the outcomes of allocation decisions are to be consistent with the requirements of justice.

12

Inadequate allocation criteria

This chapter identifies reasons for finding inadequate or erroneous those approaches to healthcare resource allocation which place exclusive or predominant emphasis on the following requirements:

- that distribution should be to everyone equally (a requirement which admits of different interpretations);
- that distribution should be in accordance with the operations of a free market in healthcare;
- that access to healthcare should depend on people's existing contribution to society;
- that distribution should be so organised as to accord either high priority to persons who for one reason or another are deemed especially *deserving of* treatment or care, or low priority (or no place) to persons deemed not to merit care. Among the latter the most vulnerable group are patients who are unconscious or who have suffered severe cognitive impairment. There is an increasing tendency to hasten the death of such patients by depriving them of sustenance as well as of medical treatment.

12.1 To each equally

Many people accord primacy to respect for equality in considering the distribution of healthcare. They think that this means that in some sense people should be treated equally. This requirement may in turn be taken to mean that either (i) everyone should get precisely the same as everyone else, or (ii) everyone should have an equal *chance* of getting what is usefully distributable. Sometimes the first interpretation of the requirement is taken to imply that if it cannot be positively satisfied then no one should get what is available. The second interpretation of the requirement is thought to be satisfied either by a selection by lottery or by a first-come-first-served system. On the face of it, the NHS operates a version of such a system.

The idea that in order to respect human equality all should be treated equally is at first sight consistent with the principles we defended in Part III. But it is also evident that the general requirement that one should treat people equally leaves unanswered questions which have to be answered if we are to have reasonable criteria of allocation. This will become clearer if we explore further the different interpretations of the requirement outlined in the previous paragraph.

The insistence that everyone should get precisely the same as everyone else is plausible in only very limited circumstances. We have argued that the principal object of a healthcare system is to return people to, or keep them in, a state of good health. But people's needs for healthcare obviously vary greatly. It may be reasonable to insist that everyone receives certain types of health-promotion material. But most healthcare has to be targeted to be of any benefit; there would be no point in offering most forms of healthcare to everyone even if it were available. And even if our concern to treat equally is limited to those in need, it does not seem reasonable to interpret that concern as requiring that if we cannot treat everyone in need we should treat no one.

If we turn to the second interpretation of the general requirement that all should be treated equally, namely the view that everyone should have an equal *chance* of obtaining what is distributable, we need to ask what is entailed by this view. Some have held that this interpretation of the requirement demands that access to healthcare should be within a single system for everyone, and that no one should be allowed to buy out of that system. It is felt that otherwise a lottery or first-come-first-served arrangement will not serve to ensure equal treatment.

There are certainly some good reasons for supporting a one-tiered health service: those who devise and administer the system and those who deliver healthcare within it will better understand its effects and be more committed to its improvement if they, too, are required to live within its limitations. It is also the case that less-than-universal rationing is more likely adversely to effect the already disadvantaged than the advantaged and thus compound existing inequalities. (Without certain safeguards – in respect of *what* is rationed – it is clear that the ability to circumvent rationing through access to private healthcare can result in a system which discriminates unacceptably.) And, finally, there is at least a *prima facie* case for saying that solidarity and social harmony would be best served by a universal scheme.

On the other hand, a set-up which uniquely confined people's access to healthcare to its public provision would appear inconsistent in allowing considerable inequalities in access to other needs such as food and education. It would also appear irrational in allowing freedom of choice to spend income on inessentials such as entertainment, while preventing expenditure on healthcare. Moreover, a strict lottery, or first-come-first-served arrangement within a single system of healthcare provision would have the effect of preventing doctors, nurses, and other healthcarers from giving any preference in the allocation of their time and energies to themselves, their families, the most disadvantaged, or those with dependents. And not only would private healthcare have to be forbidden, but people would have to be barred from leaving the country to seek healthcare elsewhere. If respect for equality is thought to have such implications it is clear that the price is unacceptably high. In general, if people are to flourish, they need a certain margin for choice among personal priorities and allowance for a diversity of life-plans and choices; some inequalities are the consequence of a degree of liberty which is to the benefit of all or most, and which is essential to the common good.

It seems clear, therefore, both that the claims of respect for equality should not be overpressed, and that they need to be interpreted by reference to other considerations, more particularly those regarding *need* for healthcare.

Respect for equality does however rightly disallow preference on the basis of race, religion, age, gender, marital status, geographic location, intelligence, quality of life, education, beliefs, social status or contribution – except where any of these genuinely affects need for healthcare. While selection on these bases is rarely advocated openly, there is some evidence that it occurs.

Such discrimination is contrary to the moral principles we defended in Part III. To make people's healthcare depend upon their membership of some privileged group is to indulge in arbitrary preference among persons, to fail to show adequate respect for the dignity of every human being, and contrary to the Golden Rule. It undermines the moral basis of community and threatens the common good. It is also contrary to traditional medical ethics: just as the Good Samaritan does not ask what the victim's ethnic and religious background is (this was part of the point of the original parable!) but simply responds to crying need, so the good physician seeks to rescue the dying and assist the sick just *as such* rather than because of their membership of some group favoured by him or by his community. What is more, since most people contribute in some way to the building up of a community's resources, including its health service, excluding some from benefiting would not only be arbitrary but could represent unjust enrichment of the preferred group at the expense of the disfavoured and thus be equivalent to theft. For these reasons many national and international policy statements are explicitly opposed to certain forms of discrimination in allocating healthcare.[1]

12.2 To each according to the free market

A 'free market' approach leaves it up to health 'providers' and 'consumers' to make their own bargains regarding the apportioning of healthcare. Health providers, on this account, may apply whatever standards they may wish to adopt – profit or income maximization, personal preferences and whims among potential patients, altruism or other private ideals. Patients, for their part, should decide for themselves what proportion of their incomes they wish to 'invest' in healthcare, and those who cannot afford all that they want may be able to fall back on charity of one kind or another. But otherwise the market will allocate according to the 'price mechanism' and the various deals people make with their fellows. The principal effect of this policy, for our present purposes, is that some people will be refused treatment because of their inability to pay and some will be given preference over others on the basis of their greater ability to pay.

An unregulated *laissez-faire* system would exemplify in a pure form free market allocation at work, but in practice, even in the most 'free market' societies, some government and professional regulation and subsidization is usual.

The principal problem with the free-market approach to healthcare allocation is that it inevitably excludes the poor. In the two following chapters, 13 and 14, we shall elaborate a case for an opposite criterion: equal treatment according to need, with some preference for the disadvantaged. Commitments to equal care and respect for the sanctity of life and for health, special concern for the disadvantaged, and solidarity more generally, are all endangered by a free-market system. It ignores the fact (see 5.3.2 above) that healthcare is to a considerable extent a social rather than purely private product. It is also very damaging to the practice of healthcare if doctor and patient relate purely as supplier and consumer, with healthworkers vetting their patients on the basis of income or insurance policies and patients viewing professionals as out to exploit them financially. It is precisely this trend in contemporary healthcare which is disturbing many practitioners and commentators. The model of the Good Samaritan stands as a radical criticism of any purely self-interested approach: while not unconcerned to ensure that the innkeeper is paid, the Good Samaritan intervened to assist the man beaten and left for dead without making any inquiry into his means.

Furthermore, healthcare is an unusual market for 'consumers': sick or dying patients are commonly desperate and thus engage in 'desperation bidding'; their information is unavoidably limited; they tend to hand over to the supplier (doctor) the decision as to what healthcare is appropriate for them, or at least to rely very heavily on his or her judgment. 'Providers' are likewise subject to various limitations identified in chapter 5 (5.3). In healthcare, then, there is rarely a real 'market bargain' after the model of the free-market.

12.3 To each according to their social contribution

Some have proposed that preference should be given to those individuals (or that section of the community) which makes the greatest contribution to the community, and conversely that those who are the greatest burden to the community should have the lowest priority. 'Social contributions' which might be taken into account include leadership, economic importance, family and charitable works; 'social burdens' might include criminal record, unemployment, welfare dependency or anti-social behaviour.[2] Typically this assessment of social value would include both the past and prospective future contributions. There is evidence that social contribution has been widely employed in the selection of patients for treatments in the UK as elsewhere.[3]

Most systematic accounts of the nature of justice would allow some preference to be given to those who make crucial social contributions: which kinds of contribution might merit preferential treatment we consider in the next section. Most accounts of justice enjoin

113

reciprocity in social relationships: e.g. a willingness (where reasonably possible) to contribute tax revenues in order to benefit from health expenditures, or a willingness to assist in a certain drug trial in return for benefiting from it. Social contribution is undoubtedly a relevant matter in distributing certain benefits, such as honours and rewards: knighthoods, for example, are not awarded randomly or according to need. Rather they purport to recognise some significant contribution to the life of the community. But to distribute services such as healthcare on such a basis risks valuing people too much in terms of their usefulness, is inconsistent with important norms and virtues which should govern the provision of healthcare, and threatens social cohesion and the common good. The virtuous physician, like the Good Samaritan, does not ask what social contribution the victim has made or is likely to make in the future; he or she simply intervenes to assist a sick or dying person.[4]

There are other difficulties with a social contribution standard. Lack of social contribution is often attributable to factors such as under-endowment with natural talents, poor education and socialization, unemployment, and overt or more subtle forms of discrimination. To exclude people who have suffered such disadvantages from consideration for some therapy is to compound their disadvantage. Those most likely to suffer from such an arrangement are the poor and the physically, mentally or ethnically handicapped. Two other relatively powerless groups will also suffer: a past social contribution criterion will necessarily discriminate against the young, whereas a future social contribution criterion will prejudice the chances of the elderly; we are opposed to both forms of discrimination.

12.4 To each according to their desert or merit

Yet another criterion, or series of criteria, which have been proposed for healthcare allocation is desert or merit. Here the notion is that certain people because of the nature of their condition or situation deserve (or do not deserve) a certain place in the healthcare queue (e.g. 'women and children first', 'young people should get preference', 'we shouldn't be wasting resources on those with severe irreversible brain damage') or that certain people *because of what they have done* merit (or fail to merit) such a place (e.g. 'smokers and drinkers shouldn't expect public health'). The various proposed criteria of desert need to be examined separately.

12.4.1 '*Women* and children first': a preference for those with dependents

The standard rule for choosing who should have spaces in the life-boats after a shipwreck was 'women *and* children first', which commonly meant women *with* children first. The inclusion of women, while it may have reflected an element of chivalry, principally expressed a concern to give preference to those providing indispensable support to others, in this case to dependent children.

The underlying notion, therefore, is that the common good will be best served by giving preferential treatment to those who are especially important for the functioning of the community. *This is an extension of the criterion of need* which we shall consider below: instead of focussing on the medical need of the patient alone, we focus upon their health needs as a prerequisite to their own welfare *and that of other people*; by caring for their health we are caring for a wider group as well. Thus in wartime preferential treatment is typically given to those regarded as most important to 'the war effort' and in natural disasters those with medical expertise and relief workers are treated first so that they can help in the treatment of others.

The policy of giving preference in everyday situations to patients with infant, elderly or handicapped dependants, is widely supported in the community and applied in practice. International human rights treaties continue to require that 'special protection' be accorded to mothers.[5] Favouring those with dependants is beneficial to society in various ways: it is in the interests of the dependants themselves (most children are better off with their parents alive and healthy), it helps preserve family bonds (which benefits family members and the community), it saves the expense of social support for the dependants, and it expresses a high social valuation of family life.

12.4.2 'Women and *children* first': a preference for the young

Most people, if asked, favour giving particular attention to the needs of the young in healthcare, usually because the young have by definition had the least opportunity to live.[6] Care of the young is a natural duty which goes to the very heart of what parenting, family and community are about. Such care is essential to the good of children and for the continuation of the community. It well expresses the high value placed on human life and on the family. At a time when respect for human life and for the family is threatened in various

ways, the provision of excellent healthcare for the young helps demonstrate a continuing or renewed commitment to these values. (A similar
case can be made for giving special attention to the needs of the handicapped.) This traditional position is supported by international human
rights instruments requiring that 'special measures of protection and
assistance' be undertaken on behalf of the young.[7]

12.4.3 A more general preference for younger over older patients

Some people favour a more general policy either of excluding persons
from certain treatments or all treatment once they have reached a
certain age, or of preference for younger over older patients. Such
an approach is widely practised here in the UK: patients over 65
(and to some extent from around 55) are far less likely to receive
renal dialysis than younger patients and than their contemporaries in
the US and on the Continent;[8] the same is true of cardiological,[9]
blood-clot and cancer treatments, and intensive care. Well-publicized
cases of 'age discrimination' in healthcare have caused considerable
public controversy, but in the professional literature writers have
long proposed policies such as the wholesale withdrawal of even
simple care from long-term geriatric patients suffering from advanced
dementia (on the British Medical Association's policy see 12.4.4
below).[10] Current trends in the NHS may well result in the further
reduction of access to healthcare for the elderly.[11]

The 'clinical' argument for an age criterion is that age is a useful
guide to the therapeutic appropriateness of an intervention and for
sorting patients according to capacity to benefit. But age is at best a
very rough guide to prognosis: it is the physiological impairments
which commonly accompany old age which affect a decline in the
average outcome from medical interventions, not age itself. Individuals vary enormously in their rate of biological ageing and it
would therefore seem more logical to use the particular, relevant,
organ/system impairments as the clinical basis rather than the surro-
gate of age. Thus dialysis patients over 65 have a better survival rate
than those between 55 and 64, and their quality of life is at least
comparable; renal transplants are as successful in the elderly as in
younger people.[12] Similarly, in many cardiological interventions it
has been found that there is little difference between young and old
patients,[13] yet the elderly are denied treatment in many programmes
supposedly because of their poor prognosis. As one leading gerontologist put it: "It seems clear that older people are at risk of being offered

inadequate or second-rate treatment simply because they are old. This is the classical condition of 'aggravated ageing'."[14]

The 'philosophical' argument for an age criterion is more complex and runs something like this: once a person has had a reasonable span of life – say eighty years – they have had a 'fair innings'; to expect and to seek more than this is unreasonable; we must come to terms with 'the human condition', our own finitude, and the inevitability of death, and not imagine we will somehow be exempt from 'change and decay'. Expecting others to foot the bill for one's aspiration to immortality, so this argument goes, is also unreasonable; indeed it represents a selfish disregard for others and for the common good. Spending on the healthcare of the elderly is already out of all proportion to their numbers. What is more, most people would, given the choice, prefer their life-time's healthcare entitlements skewed towards their youth and this is prudent. The health service should reflect this: while granting equal entitlements to all over a life-time, it should withhold 'hitech' life-prolonging treatments from the elderly and offer them only nursing and palliative care while concentrating resources on those who have yet to have 'a fair innings'.

There are a number of objections to this line of argument. First, the very notion of a 'typical' or 'reasonable' lifespan is tendentious. To a significant extent lifespan depends upon external factors such as environment, culture, technology, resources and, of course, disease. Many people want more than the average number of years of life and health, and they may well have goals in mind which suggest no shortfall in rationality or virtue: some great work they wish to finish, a desire to see their first great-grandchild born, a concern to outlive their dependent spouse, and so on. Nor would prudence necessarily counsel that the health resources to which one was entitled over a life-time be biased towards youth. Older people commonly want more medical care of various sorts – such as cardiopulmonary resuscitation – than is assumed by their doctors, nurses and relatives; they judge 'adequate quality of life' rather differently from the young. Even if some are willing in advance to forgo future care in order that more be available to themselves when they are young or to others, not everyone has this attitude.

That spending on the healthcare of the sick and dying elderly is 'disproportionate' to their numbers is hardly surprising: it accords with the purpose of healthcare; we do not complain that a disproportionate amount of the education budget goes to children! Furthermore, the elderly are, on average, the ones who have made the greatest contribution to the establishment and funding of the health service, and have made various other social contributions in part in the expectation that their healthcare needs will be accommodated by the next generation in their later years.

Our fundamental objection to an age criterion is, however, that it breaches the principles of non-discrimination, equal access to the satisfaction of needs, social solidarity and respect for the elderly. A good case can be made for a complaint that many contemporary Western societies, and perhaps Britain more than most, undervalue their older members and shows signs of ageist prejudice. The elderly, already naturally weak (especially in a competitive society), are devalued by fashion, commerce and the media, disempowered by political institutions, inadequately provided for by social welfare, and abandoned to low-grade accommodation and care. Their experience, past contributions and present wisdom are ignored, while the young, productive and physically perfect are idolized. All too often ageing is treated as a kind of social 'leprosy' to be denied and warded off at all costs (with cosmetics, face-lifts, exercise, etc.) and, when no longer deniable, is deemed to merit social excommunication. In such an environment an age criterion in health distribution may reflect and itself generate further prejudice against an already vulnerable and relatively powerless group. Here in Britain the elderly are demonstrably less politically powerful than their 'gray-power' contemporaries across the Atlantic. They are therefore much more likely to suffer scape-goating, immoral abandonment or neglect, even euthanasia, especially in the face of spiralling costs. We believe that any further pressure in this direction should be resisted now by a strong insistence that age will not be a criterion of healthcare distribution.

As Christians we would want to add a further argument to this secular case for non-discrimination on the basis of age. By caring for the sick elderly we express such fundamental values as equal respect for persons from conception to natural death, the dignity which belongs to every living human being, special concern for the vulnerable and powerless, solidarity with those who suffer, and support for the institution of the family. But perhaps most powerfully we exhibit the traditional virtue of 'pietas' or 'reverence', that is, filial affection and duty, respect, even veneration, for elders, gratitude for their contribution, readiness to acknowledge their wisdom and experience. The virtue of 'piety' is demonstrably in decline and one the importance of which needs, we think, to be reaffirmed. High quality healthcare for the elderly can be a powerful demonstration of such reverence at work.

12.4.4 'We shouldn't be wasting resources on those with severe brain damage': mental ability and minimum quality of life as a basis for rationing

It is frequently proposed that preference should be given to those who are conscious or are likely to recover consciousness or are likely to gain the greatest improvement in quality of life, and that treatment should be minimized for or even denied to those who are permanently unconscious or who are not expected to gain much improvement in quality of life from treatment. Such proposals are already implemented in some quarters, and in recent years there has been considerable controversy, including litigation, over the standard of care due to the permanently unconscious and others at a low ebb: in particular, litigation concerning whether assisted nutrition (tubefeeding) and hydration, as well as medical treatment, should be withdrawn.

There may of course be many reasons for reducing the level of strictly medical *treatment* of the permanently or commonly unconscious and those who have suffered extensive and irreversible mental and physical damage: there may be no more 'healing' that medicine can do, so that therapeutic measures have become futile and only nursing and palliative care remain appropriate; or the treatment may be so gravely burdensome for the patient or others as not to be warranted. It might also be argued that while such patients are not beyond the possibility of non-burdensome medical assistance (e.g. simple interventions such as antibiotics to ensure that they do not deteriorate further), such assistance is still inappropriate because there is no hope of recovering even an approximation to 'health'; or that any therapeutic benefit from such treatment will be less than that gained by almost any other deployment of the resource. Some go further and assert that the continued living of such patients places such a burden upon themselves or others that they would be 'better off dead'; they therefore are no longer fitting subjects of care and should be allowed (or even assisted) to die as soon as possible. It is only the last of these positions that we wish to emphatically reject here.

Many contemporary 'liberal' theories (such as those examined in Chapters 6 to 8) take the possession of exercisable abilities of understanding and choice to be a condition for a human life to have value, so that those who are unconscious or who have gravely impaired intellectual abilities have lives without value. The under-standing of the person, morality and community which we have offered in Chapters 9 to 11 rejects such a discriminatory distinction between human beings. These patients are still living human persons with dignity and with needs, however diminished may be their capacity to participate in most human goods; even the perma-nently unconscious have continuing interests albeit they are unaware of them (see 10.1).

Traditional medical ethics has required that all living human beings be treated with equal concern and respect, however intellectually or otherwise handicapped they may be, whether they are conscious or not, and however low is their present or prospective quality of life. To adopt a minimum quality of life criterion for healthcare allocation would have major moral and social implications. A whole range of patients suffer impairment of mental abilities to various degrees with various degrees of permanence; a larger group of the mentally handi-capped and psychiatrically ill suffer conditions which are intellectually and socially impoverishing; and the class of those with low quality of life is both arbitrary and very elastic. If mental abilities and a certain quality of life are to be regarded as necessary requirements for sharing in healthcare resources, a large and potentially widening group of people will be excluded. And if we accept that humanity *per se* is no longer sufficient qualification for sharing in the benefits of community life, then qualities such as intelligence, social relation-ships or productivity, all at some arbitrarily determined level, may come to be regarded as necessary for the receipt of healthcare.[15]

In chapter 8 we examined the utilitarian policy of giving preference to the patient(s) expected to enjoy, or the treatment, institution or system expected to yield, the greatest improvement in quality of life or well-being (per unit spent on healthcare), and of assessing certain patients as having lives not worth living and sicknesses not worth treating (those with 'negative quality of life'). We need not rehearse our criticisms of this approach: suffice it to say here that the very notion of 'quality of life' is highly tendentious, and attempts to apply it to healthcare allocation are dogged with problems both theoretical and practical. Furthermore, like an age criterion, the adop-tion of a mental ability or quality of life standard would discourage compliance with principles of morality such as those forbidding killing, harming and abandoning, and those requiring respect for the dignity and equality of all, preservation of life and promotion of health, and support for the disadvantaged. Like an age criterion, it could encourage the abandonment of some of the most vulnerable members of the community, contrary to the values traditionally expressed by communities through their healthcare systems, and contrary to the best traditions of healthcare, and ultimately to the very *raison d'être* of society itself.

That being so, it is a cause for serious concern that for more than a decade now the British Medical Association (BMA) has advanced and developed a position which gravely discriminates against the severely mentally impaired. Thus in their 1988 Report on *Euthanasia*,[16] which became BMA policy, we read that

> '... some patients have permanently lost all capacity for *the conscious quality of life that constitutes being fully human*... We have stopped short of saying that such a state ought to be terminated by a *positive* act.' [Para. 131.1; emphasis added.]

By implication, however, it is clearly regarded as allowable that doctors aim to end the lives of severely mentally damaged patients by deliberately depriving them of the care needed to sustain their lives. But such a course of conduct constitutes intentional killing and as such is morally indistinguishable from killing patients by a positive act.

Paragraph 134 of the Report *Euthanasia* went on to endorse the policy of offering 'hydration and cuddling', but no nutrition, for babies judged to lack 'the capacity for meaningful human life' [para. 133]. They were deemed to lack that capacity if they lacked 'the capacity to love and be loved. If this is not present and is never going to be then it is clear that the child lacks that crucial engagement with persons that constitutes a basis for ethically significant life.' Those who lack 'ethically significant life' are regarded as the legitimate targets of a policy of starvation. A policy of sedating and starving handicapped newborn babies had long been established in certain pediatric units since the 1970s, so the BMA Working Party's failure in 1988 to acknowledge that one may intentionally kill by deliberately depriving people of the basic care (particularly nourishment) which they need may well have been motivated by a desire not to identify the moral reality of what was occurring.

The logic of treating as ethically respectable the practice of intentionally killing patients by omission of care has most recently been carried forward by the BMA Ethics Committee in its Report *Withholding and Withdrawing Lifeprolonging Medical Treatment. Guidance for decision making*[17] (hereinafter *Guidance*). There the practice is envisaged as a policy applicable to:

- non-terminally ill patients in what is called a 'persistent vegetative state';
- non-terminally ill patients 'in a state of very low awareness closely resembling PVS';
- non-terminally ill patients who have suffered severe irreversible brain damage;
- non-terminally ill patients with advanced senile dementia.

Individual patients in all these ill-defined categories may, according to the BMA, be judged to be suitable candidates for death by starvation by having previously established tubefeeding withdrawn.

The duty to provide basic care of a patient one has admitted into one's care is more fundamental than the duty to provide medical treatment. As we have acknowledged, doctors may reach a point in their care of a patient when further *medical* treatment can neither cure, modify the patient's condition or alleviate symptoms. But the patient remains alive and is not dying. Elementary respect for the life of the patient requires that one offer him or her basic care. Tubefeeding, even when it requires some measure of medical management, as such provides no more than nourishment, the purpose of which is not treatment but sustaining the life of the patient. There is one main reason for withdrawing tubefeeding of patients who are not terminally ill and who are being effectively nourished in this way: to put an end to their lives. If tubefeeding in those circumstances is said to be futile it is because one judges the very life of the patient to be worthless. And indeed it is that judgement on the lives of severely cognitively impaired patients which seems to motivate BMA policy.[18] In saying this we do not imply that there are no circumstances in which it is reasonable to withdraw tubefeeding. There are: when it fails to nourish the patient; when the patient is very close to death (though hydration should be maintained at least as a palliative measure); and when the available means of tubefeeding prove excessively burdensome to the patient.

The import of BMA policy has been somewhat disguised in public debate by their defining tubefeeding as medical treatment and redefining the objective of ordinary care as 'comfort' rather than the sustenance and support of a life. But neither move is defensible. People who want to say tubefeeding is medical treatment commonly give as reasons for doing so the fact that it is 'intrusive' and the fact that it supplies for a natural function (in this case swallowing). Yet the BMA clearly allows that a hygiene measure such as insertion of a urinary catheter is part of basic care; but the catheter is obviously both intrusive and supplies for a natural function.[19] The second move – that of redefining the objective of basic care as 'comfort' rather than sustaining a life – is a piece of arbitrary stipulation which has no intelligible motive other than that of trying to induce people to believe that the withdrawal of tubefeeding is not the withdrawal of basic care.

In section 25 of the *Guidance*, Health Authorities are recommended to provide local guidelines (on withdrawal of treatment and tube-feeding) which are presumably intended to reflect BMA policy. In addition to guidelines, Health Authorities are enjoined to have 'a system of audit to ensure that the guidelines are being followed'. Managers are told that they have 'an obligation to investigate promptly' evidence of 'anomalous patterns of decision making' in their facilities. All this seems calculated to marginalise doctors who object to withdrawing tubefeeding in order to end their patients' lives. Doubtless significant sums of money could be saved in care of the elderly if hospital trust managers were to follow BMA *Guidance*.

12.4.5 'Smokers and drinkers shouldn't expect public health': reward for personal responsibility

In Chapter 10 (10.9) we argued that primary moral responsibility for healthcare rests with the individual. Moral agency and human flourishing demand self-determination and the following of one's conscience and chosen commitments: people should therefore not be forever looking to others to make decisions for them or to 'bail them out'. Nor should others too readily do so: however well-meaning it might be, paternalistic welfare (including healthcare) can infantilize people and discourage them from acting responsibly. There are also some very practical reasons for encouraging people to be responsible in this area: there is more and more evidence that life-style choices are a significant factor in determining health status, and strains on health resources would be alleviated by people adopting healthier practices. While healthier life-style cannot eliminate vulnerability to nature or the harmful decisions of others, many injuries or illnesses are partly or wholly self-inflicted or the result of self-neglect.

As a result it is increasingly proposed that people's responsibility for their own ill-health should be taken into account when allocating healthcare: those patients who are judged to have brought their condition upon themselves could be 'put to the end of the queue' behind those who have done their best to look after their own health, or they might even be excluded from public health altogether. Examples of patients who would be affected by this standard are: substance-abusers (such as smokers, over-drinkers, drug-addicts, those who choose to eat unhealthily); those who engage in physically risky activities (certain sports, adventures, sunbathing, promiscuous sexual activity, driving without a seatbelt); those who voluntarily mutilate themselves in some way or consent to this (tattoos, sterilization, attempted suicide); and those who neglect their own health (through inappropriate dressing or lack of exercise, for example).

While in favour of efforts to encourage people to take responsibility for their health, we would argue against the application of a personal responsibility criterion in healthcare allocation for a number of reasons. First, causation in disease is very complex: rarely is there a single, specific cause. Many diseases, such as lung cancer, are the result of multiple factors such as genetic predisposition, environment, psychological state and life-style choices such as smoking, and not simply the last of these. Secondly, even were *causality* wholly or partly attributable to decisions of the agent, difficulties arise with the attribution of *responsibility* or blame. People's knowledge about the health-risks associated with various activities is limited, and the effects of their risk-taking may be out of all proportion to their reasonable expectations. Furthermore, though we are free agents we do not make our choices independently of our bodies, history and the community which helps to shape our long-term values and our more immediate choices; we have different degrees of control over our lives and differing consciousness of our powers and responsibilities. A sixteen year old cadet sailor who wakes up after a night of high spirits has reduced responsibility for the tattoos he finds on his body the next morning; smoking is only half-heartedly discouraged by our community today, and was not discouraged at all decades ago when many people became addicted. And health neglect is frequently a symptom of some other disease or disadvantage. There is a risk of pharisaically blaming alcoholics and smokers when the community is partly responsible for their plight, and when it subsidizes other health risks such as mountain-climbing and over-eating.

There is also the difficulty of establishing what kinds of risks are unreasonable ones. Certain risk-taking is, after all, morally necessary; other risk-taking is clearly imprudent; and yet other risks are more or less optional. Certain voluntary risks are encouraged by society (e.g. fire fighting, marathon running, transportation, surgery); others are tolerated or ignored (e.g. over-working); others are halfheartedly discouraged (e.g. sexual promiscuity, smoking); and still others are deplored (e.g. heroin abuse). Furthermore, those who are ill may already have made significant, even disproportionate, contributions to common funds with a reasonable expectation of healthcover, so that excluding them would be unjust: the sales taxes smokers pay could be an example of this.

But even were a person's injury due to a manifestly unreasonable risk, and even had the person made little contribution to the community, for the community to abandon him or her in sickness would amount to repudiating solidarity with the sick and mercy towards them. Once again, this would run contrary to good medical practice which has always treated those who have attempted suicide, have drug problems or sexually transmitted diseases. The Good Samaritan, while never denying that people should take reasonable care of themselves, does not ask whether the victim 'brought it on himself' by walking down a dark alley at night-time or otherwise failing to take adequate precautions. Likewise, however disagreeable, negligent or morally repugnant some patients may seem, the health professional's mission is to treat the sick as such. If a community wishes to discourage certain risk-taking, other means of doing so, such as education and the law, would seem better suited to this purpose than the health service.

On balance, then, we believe that any attempt to allocate healthcare on the basis of personal responsibility or irresponsibility is fraught with theoretical and practical difficulties. This does not preclude a community requiring those who knowingly choose risky life-styles or behaviours to make certain additional contributions, e.g. a tax on tobacco at a rate calculated to cover the additional cost of the risk-takers' healthcare.

13

To each according to his/her need

Building on what was said in Chapter 10 about the importance of distinguishing between genuine and spurious healthcare needs, this chapter offers guidelines, by reference to the character of healthcare need, for arriving at orders of priority between patients, between patient groups, and between treatments. The requirement that there should be equality of access applies only after one has determined which patients are most in need of healthcare. Considerations of effectiveness and efficiency should influence what is done to meet healthcare need, though they should not determine priority of need. For it remains the case that those who can benefit little therapeutically, such as the dying and the severely disabled, nonetheless have 'healthcare needs' which it is important to meet since 'healthcare' is for such patients the most appropriate expression of our respect for them and solidarity with them – values which should inform the whole healthcare system.

In Chapter 10 we argued that the satisfaction of healthcare needs is basic to the very logic of healthcare as a practice, *what it is for*. In Chapter 11 we argued that both justice adequately understood and respect for human persons requires the provision of healthcare in response to such need; that any just society will seek to ensure this for all members of the community; and that while lack of resources and competing goals may mean that not all healthcare needs will be met or met as well as they might otherwise be, any failure to satisfy healthcare need requires strong justification. It is not surprising, therefore, that need has been the traditional basis for the allocation of healthcare and remains the one most favoured by practitioners and the general public; it has also been the stated object of the NHS from the beginning to this day. The most recent set of arrangements, outlined in *The New NHS*, identifies the first task of health authorities as that of 'assessing the health needs of the local population', and the second as that of 'drawing up a strategy for meeting those needs, in the form of a Health Improvement Programme ... and ensuring delivery of the NHS contribution to it'.[1]

It must of course be recognized that needs claims can conflict, and those with needs can be unwitting rivals for some scarce resource; that unless there are rational limits to needs claims they lose their moral, rhetorical and political force; and that some basis for identifying, moderating and sorting needs is therefore essential. We began to outline this in Chapter 10: by careful attention to the nature of genuine healthcare needs, the reasonable and unreasonable ways of satisfying these, and what is appropriate by way of individual and community provision, it is possible to identify and to some extent moderate genuine needs in this area.

What does the process of doing so look like in practice? It begins from the injunction: when making distributions of healthcare, decisionmakers should assess both patients and treatments, first and foremost on the basis of need for healthcare. An individual doctor, for instance, would begin by assessing his or her patient's own medical condition (rather than bank account, contributions to worthy causes, or position in life) and the therapeutically appropriate ways of assisting. Such an assessment will include matters such as: the patient's present health, relative to what is reasonably to be expected; the risk and imminence of death or major damage; the seriousness of actual or potential damage and associated pain and disability; the patient's likely health (similarly assessed) after each of the various treatment and non-treatment options; and the benefits and burdens associated with each treatment option or non-treatment. The doctor will *not* take into account the factors examined and criticized as inappropriate in the previous chapter. Treatments which are unnecessary or ineffective or less effective than others in relation to need or only barely useful or of unproven value or harmful will, generally speaking, not be applied. In these ways the idea of need can begin to set the parameters for national and local budgetary requirements and individual entitlements or rights.

Patients, healthworkers and health services should give priority to people's most important needs over their less important ones, and to those with more important needs over those with less important ones. Judgments will have to be made about each patient on the basis outlined in the previous paragraph; similarities and differences between the patients in these terms would then be identified. The healthcare need criterion thus provides a general standard for sorting needs. Put simply: *medical needs should be addressed in order of importance and preference given to the patient in greater need.* Of course, clear and important as this principle is, in the realities of day-to-day practice it can be very difficult to apply and so requires considerable unpacking.

A person can *need* healthcare in different ways and to different degrees. Obviously certain kinds of healthcare for certain patients will be more or less crucial or urgent in that damage to life or health will be more or less imminent without it. Thus *urgency*, arising in particular from the imminence of death or major damage without treatment, is properly part of the assessment of healthcare need. One patient may need a treatment immediately, while another could do without it for a time. Giving priority to those with reversible risk of death has long been standard healthcare practice (e.g. in the distribution of intensive care, organs for transplant, lifesaving operations.). Where choices are unavoidable, a similar case (which need not be spelt out here) can be made for giving preference, *ceteris paribus*, to the patient

- whose need is more urgent,
- who is more likely to benefit therapeutically from the available treatment,
- who is likely to gain the greater or longer therapeutic benefit from the treatment,
- who is likely to suffer the lesser burden from the treatment,
- who is likely to suffer the greater harm without the treatment,
- who is less at risk of various ill-effects from the treatment,
- who is likely to gain the same therapeutic benefit from less of the treatment,
- who is likely to need the treatment for a shorter time or less frequently,
- who has fewer or no alternative avenues of satisfying the need, or
- who is more likely to infect others if untreated.

A similar set of priority criteria may be drawn up for comparing rival patient groups, and for determining which kinds of treatment (and, therefore, institutional arrangements) should be given priority. With each priority rule, and after the application of whichever are relevant, an equality criterion (first-come-first-served or lottery) would be the appropriate residual principle of distribution.

Certain kinds of healthcare will be more or less likely to yield more or less therapeutic benefit, for longer or shorter periods. Where needs are roughly equal, it is logical to seek the most effective and efficient way of satisfying them; where health resources are limited, to endeavour to get the most therapeutic benefit from them. This is the kind of 'efficiency calculation' or 'technical reasoning' which we argued in Chapter 8 (8.8) *is* possible and sensible – the kernel of truth in the utilitarian or economic approach. So there will, after all, be a substantial place for the kinds of health-gain and cost-benefit analysis examined and criticized in Chapter 8, as long as it is not engaged in reductively (e.g. equating need with capacity to gain a certain number of QALYs). On the other hand, as we have repeatedly noted, there are sometimes values in doing the apparently inefficient even in health-care: it may, for instance, be an expression of solidarity or of esteem, of equal care and respect, of love for a dying person.

Giving priority in healthcare allocation to those who are most likely to benefit therapeutically or to those who will benefit the longest or to those who will benefit the most from the fewest resources, has long been widely supported amongst practitioners and commentators. Thus, for instance, patients with a poor prognosis (such as 'the dying') are not normally given highly intrusive or expensive treatments. The extent to which patients can benefit therapeutically, though an important consideration in identifying healthcare need, cannot exclusively determine what is to count as healthcare need. *In circumstances in which we can do very little for a patient, we still have an obligation at least to do what we can. This explains why we care even for people at 'a very low ebb': it ensures their continued participation in those goods in which they are capable of sharing; it maintains our bonds of community with them; it expresses benevolence and respect for their dignity.*

A needs criterion ought not to be used to mask other standards such as social contribution or quality of life. Many contemporary assessments of healthcare need in relation to comatose, severely handicapped, substance abusing, 'socially undesirable' and elderly patients probably reflect some kind of 'quality of life' or 'social value' judgment which evaluates the needs of such patients at a significant discount from those of more able patients. The range of cases in which this occurs may well grow in the future. When resources are limited, there is a temptation to 'tighten' standards of need until the number of patients who satisfy the healthcare need criterion is reduced to match neatly the number of resources available; this has demonstrably been the case regarding dialysis in Britain as elsewhere.

The adoption of a needs criterion provides a basis not just for allocating existing healthcare resources but for establishing the reasonable limits to budgets and orienting future practice. For instance, the present system might well be criticized for being too 'reactive' rather than 'pro-active', relying as it does upon patients themselves to be aware of and to report their needs before any care is offered them; it might be argued that we should be more active in targetting resources to those who already have or are at risk of certain conditions whether or not they are yet aware of it. Some progress in this direction has already been made: but a needs criterion would counsel further improvements.

Need is always a quality of individuals and if it is difficult enough to assess need at the bedside and to compare individuals, it becomes even more problematic at each level of aggregation from particular families to medical practices to hospitals to health authority localities to the nation. This points again to the importance of both sensitivity to need as the overriding framework for healthcare allocation *at all levels of the health service* and an adequate understanding of 'healthcare need' in order to identify priorities.

Conclusion to Chapters 12 and 13

Having explored the nature of human choice, persons, community and medicine, we have argued that a distributively just health service will (as far as possible) ensure access for all members of the community to care sufficient to meet their healtheare needs; and we have tried to specify what this level and these needs may be. We have suggested some ways in which needs may be identified, moderated and sorted, and ways in which they may reasonably be satisfied, as well as ways in which it would be unjust to seek to satisfy them. In these chapters we have argued further that healthcare should be allocated according to healthcare need, irrespective of factors such as race, religion, social contribution, age, consciousness, intelligence, quality of life, provider-whim and ability to pay. Possible exceptions to this needs-egalitarian approach would be: preference in favour of the disadvantaged (see further Chapter 15) and preference for those upon whom others crucially rely. We are now in a position to consider some issues other than distributive justice which have an important bearing on the way we should allocate healthcare resources.

14

Other considerations in healthcare allocation

The provision of healthcare should be seen as just one element in the common good which encompasses the ensemble of conditions necessary and favourable to the flourishing of all members of society. A society has therefore to make provision also for the realization of other basic human goods. Moreover, the requirements of distributive justice are not the only requirements which need to be borne in mind in healthcare allocation. Respect for other values and for basic human rights must also be borne in mind. Yet as a society *and precisely in the allocation of healthcare resources* we act contrary to respect for the right to life and bodily integrity (in funding abortion, embryo experimentation, sterilization and other forms of mutilation). Furthermore, an increasing body of evidence has emerged in recent years of such frequent neglect of the frail elderly that it appears to be systemic. The most extreme expression of this tendency is the policy of withdrawing tubefeeding from those who have suffered severe mental impairment but who are not terminally ill and who are thereby caused to die of starvation. In the case of patients who are irreversibly unconscious this policy has been approved by the Courts in *Bland* and the series of cases which followed. It is vital to the restoration of a just policy of care for the frail elderly and all those judged to have a 'poor quality of life' that the *Bland* judgement should be reversed.

14.1 Introduction

The principal concern in any ethical assessment of healthcare allocation is distributive justice, In chapters 9 to 13 we sought to outline
an adequate systematic understanding of distributive justice in healthcare. Distributive justice is not, however, the only kind of ethical
consideration relevant to healthcare allocation. In previous chapters,
for instance, we have seen that a range of core values are expressed
through the health system which might not be captured by a narrow
conception of the purposes of medicine and its just rationing. Likewise
we must consider competing social goals and basic human rights
which might be affected by any allocation scheme or principle, or by
the implementation of any proposal.

14.2 Competing social goals

Much of the responsibility for the provision of modern healthcare is
delegated to or claimed from 'society' or the state. In Chapter 11 we
explored the basis of this responsibility and expectation, proposing
that there is need for a rich conception of the good of human
persons in community. As with the well-functioning family, so in
the well-functioning society, people act for others' true interests and
well-being as part of their own well-being; they adopt a perspective
which takes account of the well-being of all members, making it
crucial to their own identity and self-fulfilment. The members of a
society view the flourishing of each and thus the participation of
each in those basic goods they have in common as part of their own
good, their *common good*, and so seek to co-operate in the provision
of that ensemble of conditions necessary for the fulfilment of all of
the members. Any society and government's claim to allegiance
from its citizens is contingent upon there being an appreciable level
of commitment to the common good so understood.

Thus *the common good* refers to the flourishing of the members of a
community and thus to the various goods-in-common pursued by
them and the complex of conditions, institutions and projects which
are necessary for that flourishing.[1] As the common good embraces,
contributes to, and is indispensable for the good of every individual,
it cannot be reduced simply to the will of the voting majority or
'the greatest good for the greatest number'. Further, the notion of
the common good excludes the idea that members of a community

are essentially rivals with each other or with the community as a whole in achieving their good, an idea which is something of a commonplace in the kind of theories examined in Part II. Rather, we have in mind a conception of the common good for which the purpose of society and government is ensuring co-operation in the provision for each of the conditions and opportunities to live a fully human life. We have argued that this must include the satisfaction of needs which individuals cannot provide for themselves, such as healthcare.

Of course health, with the consequent need for healthcare, is only one of the ingredient goods required for human well-being. A good community or society has to make complex provision for other goods. The diverse goods of any political community will include justice and peace, requiring:

- *leadership* (including legitimate decisionmaking processes whereby various conflicting rights, claims, interests and duties can be negotiated or adjudicated);
- promotion of the goods of *other communities* (through international organizations, foreign aid, diplomacy);
- *defence* against external enemies (by diplomacy, defence forces, border control);
- maintenance of *law and order* (by legislation, policing, courts);
- promotion and regulation of *economic* activities (by foreign exchange, banking regulation, licensing, subsidies);
- ensuring access to *welfare* needs (by regulating, subsidizing and directly providing for healthcare, unemployment support, housing, family support...);
- *distributing property* justly (by progressive taxation and welfare, and by property laws).

Vital also to the common good are respect for the good of truth (requiring sound educational institutions, for example), the enjoyment of beauty, the flourishing of arts and skills, and freedom of religious practice.

A complex common good is not realisable without considerable organization and the establishment of often quite elaborate institutions, systems and policies of decisionmaking and implementation. There will be considerable negotiation and trade-off. But the important point to note here is that healthcare is only one among several goods-in-common which serve the common good and which will inevitably compete with other goods when resources are scarce; it is not and should not be seen as the only or principal social good.

14.3 Basic rights must be respected

In Chapter 11 we argued for a right to healthcare within certain confines. Other human rights – such as the right to life – might further support the right to healthcare, and these rights together would constrain proposed healthcare allocations in certain ways. However these are by no means the only human rights. No resolution of issues of distribution can be morally acceptable which involves people acting contrary to the basic human rights of some human beings. Some analysts have shown the cost-efficiency of aborting handicapped children,[2] the utility to be gained by forcing people against their wills to donate organs for 'redistribution',[3] and the public health and finance advantages of compulsory universal screening for HIV and quarantining of those with the disease.[4] One could easily imagine a case for brainwashing campaigns and laws requiring compulsory exercise, blood transfusions, operations, diets, and the like, all in the name of a more efficient health system. But all of these would infringe basic rights and civil liberties in serious ways. In the sections which follow we identify some areas where human rights are especially endangered by certain contemporary trends and proposals, in particular the rights to life and equal treatment.

14.4 Directly homicidal or harmful healthcare allocations

In medical situations there are lots of opportunities to save life and improve health; there are likewise many ways and means to kill or harm people, whether by actively doing something harmful or by neglecting to do something one was dutybound to do. Obvious examples of homicidal or harmful 'medical' practices are abortion, embryo experimentation, euthanasia, sterilisation and other mutilation (e.g. surgery for 'gender re-assignment'), and detrimental experimentation. When some of these harmful practices have considerable amounts of our scarce healthcare resources devoted to them this further subverts rather than fosters the common good. A society which supported a sound understanding of the common good would seek to suppress not subsidise such activities.

Some people might argue for harmful or even homicidal activity as part of a programme of more 'efficient' healthcare allocation: they might, for instance, regard this as licit as long as the agent gives consent (for whatever reasons) or should consent (e.g. because they are an unreasonable burden upon others) or can be presumed to consent (e.g. because they are incompetent and judged to be 'better off dead') and 'the greater good of the greater number' would thereby be served. Thus it might be suggested that all patients over a certain age, or below a certain quality of life, or requiring healthcare resources above a certain threshold, should be denied all further treatment and the lives of some (those with a very low 'quality of life') should be terminated.

Such a policy would, however, run contrary to the norm of common morality against killing the innocent, a norm which has historically informed medical practice, been stated in all codes of medical ethics, and generally defended by law and society. Thus traditional medical ethics held that physicians might not kill their patients even to relieve their pain,[5] and that they might not act as public torturers or executioners. This traditional norm is supported by the understanding of morality we outlined in Chapters 9 to 11: to kill an innocent human being is to act contrary to the most fundamental norm of justice. To compromise this norm is to compromise what is indispensable to the common good. There can therefore be no room for such compromise even if the ulterior motive is a good one, e.g. to save enough resources to be able to promote the health and life of others or to use for some other worthwhile project. Such a choice breaches not only the norm against killing the innocent but also those against harming and doing evil to achieve good and those requiring impartiality and care for others. Anyone who accepts these norms of common morality (whether on grounds such as those we have proposed or on some other ground) should judge that healthcare rationing by intentionally killing or harming patients, either by act or by deliberate omission intended to end life or damage health, is immoral.

14.5 Indirectly homicidal and harmful healthcare allocations

Not all healthcare choices which foreseeably result in death are homicidal in intent. A doctor who must choose which of two patients will receive some scarce lifesaving resource (e.g. an intensive care bed) does *not* intend the death of the other patient; a healthcare administrator who decides to spend less on intensive care and more on hip replacements may well not be blameworthy for the deaths of all those who might have missed out on intensive care; and so on. The positive duty of care is not absolute: people are not bound to strive to save life at all times and in all circumstances, at whatever cost to themselves and others, and by whatever means; there are various good grounds for withholding or withdrawing treatments, one of which can be insufficiency of resources. When doctors (or planners or administrators) make a distribution of resources and death results earlier than it might otherwise have done for some patients, the hastening of their deaths need not be why such a course of action was chosen; nor need there have been any reckless disregard for this unintended side-effect. The deaths may or may not have been foreseen, but if they were not a part of the doctor's purposes, nor the means used to achieve those purposes, nor unjustly or negligently ignored or devalued in pursuit of those purposes, then the doctor is not to blame for the deaths.

On the other hand, some allocations might result from a judgment that a certain patient's life or health is less valuable than others', that certain persons would be better off dead, or that others would be better off were they dead. In that case, shortening patients' lives or harming them may well be part or the whole of the agent's intent when distributing the healthcare resource. Furthermore, where a person has made certain undertakings or assumed certain roles regarding the care of another, any neglect to fulfil that duty could amount to the (moral and legal) equivalent of homicide or maiming by omission.[6] For the reasons outlined already, this would be immoral.

14.6 Punitive healthcare allocations

Punishment is likewise an inappropriate motive in healthcare allocation. If a doctor or administrator were to refuse a patient or patient group a share of healthcare resources as private punishment for some past harm that patient (or those associated with him) had done to that doctor (or those associated with her), this would clearly be immoral. In Chapter 12 (12.4.5) we considered the case of patients whose self-inflicted injuries may tempt health professionals to refuse them healthcare. Here, as we saw, the argument is complex, partly because attribution of causation and responsibility in this area is commonly complicated. Sometimes personal responsibility or irresponsibility may be a relevant basis for discrimination: e.g. where it reliably indicates prognosis or likelihood of future compliance with a proposed therapeutic regime. But in other cases refusal to treat those who 'brought their sickness on themselves' may represent a kind of punishment which it is no part of the rôle of healthcarer to dispense. Healthcare allocation ought not to be used by healthworkers as a vehicle for a kind of judgmentalism and resentment towards certain patients which amounts to something like an act of retribution.

14.7 Prejudiced healthcare allocations

As we have seen, an ethical principle of recurring significance for healthcare allocation is impartiality between persons. Just as we have no reason to deny that any of the basic goods is one we can in principle participate in, so we have no reason to deny that the basic goods are really good and fit matters of concern on the part of other people. Arbitrary preferences among persons are excluded by the principle known traditionally as 'the Golden Rule'. This does not mean that there is not reasonable scope for self-preference or preference for one's family, friends or community; but when all reasonable allowance is made for that, this principle remains 'a pungent critique of selfishness, special pleading, double standards, hypocrisy, indifference to the good of others whom one could easily help ('passing by on the other side'), and all the other manifold forms of egoistic and group bias'.[7] In healthcare distribution, this principle would exclude allocations on the basis of race, sex, social class, social contribution, 'co-operativeness', or any other arbitrary playing of favourites among persons.

14.8 Those at risk: the frail elderly, the handicapped, the mentally ill, the poor

There is evidence that some recent healthcare reforms have put at risk needy and relatively powerless groups such as the elderly, the handicapped, the chronically ill, the mentally ill, and the poor. There is a great deal of anecdotal evidence of declining access for these groups to some health services and a shift of responsibility for their care back upon 'the community' (i.e. self, family and friends, neighbours, charities, local authorities). There is increasingly well-documented evidence of discrimination against the elderly in the NHS, particularly the frail elderly.[8]

Any trend in the health system to abandoning or putting at risk the frail elderly, the handicapped, the mentally ill or the poor must be resisted. It is immoral for several reasons. First, as we suggested in chapter 11 (11.4) and will elaborate in chapter 15, the way these groups are treated is a litmus test for the justice of the system as a whole. Would I think the healthcare budget and its distribution fair if I (or someone I loved) were in healthcare need, especially if I were among the weakest in the community (i.e. sick with a chronic, disabling and expensive ailment, elderly, poor and illiterate)? Would I think it were fair if I were one who would go without under the proposed arrangements?

Secondly, any failure of care for such groups is likely to encourage more behaviour of the kinds criticized in the previous sections – homicidal, harmful, neglectful, punitive, prejudiced – towards those same groups. Resources should be distributed in a way which is adequate to sustain a level of care for the dependent elderly, the handicapped and the mentally ill which will reduce the temptations to act towards them in ways fundamentally contrary to justice and human solidarity.

Thirdly, as such groups already commonly suffer discrimination and disadvantage of various sorts, any such tendency in the health system would further compound this ill-fortune and/or injustice and further endanger the health of groups already considerably at risk.

One group increasingly at grave risk is the group of those patients who have suffered severe mental impairment. Their vulnerability to injustice has greatly increased as a result of judicial decisions in the case of Tony Bland in 1993. He had been left permanently unconscious after the Hillsborough football stadium disaster in 1989. The courts decided that he could have his tubefeeding and hydration discontinued and he died nine days later. The judges concluded, with little serious argument, that tubefeeding is a 'medical treatment'; that when applying medical treatments, doctors may follow 'informed and responsible medical opinion'; that such opinion may be gleaned from the latest discussion paper of the BMA's ethics committee; and that such opinion now counsels or allows the withdrawal of all treatment to PVS patients such as Tony Bland because treatment, indeed life, is not in his best interests.

We have already noted that there can be good reasons to withhold or withdraw medical treatment, e.g. where treatments are medically futile or disproportionately burdensome to the patient or beyond the resources of the institution or community. But for doctors to withdraw food or care which is neither futile nor overly burdensome, with the sole objective of ending the patient's life is, and has traditionally been classified as, homicide. Yet in the Bland case it was openly recognized that the intention of withdrawing tubefeeding was precisely to bring about death. The courts effectively allowed passive euthanasia or euthanasia by omission.[9] Commentators at the time noted the unseemly enthusiasm for this new direction among some of the judges, prompted especially by the 'friend of the court' briefed by the Attorney-General. Some wondered whether cost-cutting played a part in the attitude of the Government. Budgeters and planners in the NHS have long recognized that the cost of care of PVS patients is considerable; press estimates put it at £40 to £150 million a year. The cost of Tony Bland's care was clearly a consideration in the minds of courts in the decision to stop caring for Tony Bland. Counsel for the Attorney General argued that 'all treatment decisions have to be made within the limits of available resources, and that it will inevitably be necessary to make choices as to the allocation of those resources as between the competing claims of patients... this is a fact of life which Courts, like doctors and hospital administrators unfortunately cannot ignore...'. The Master of the Rolls declared that 'an objective assessment of Mr Bland's best interests... [would give weight], if altruism still lives, to a belief that finite resources are better devoted to enhancing life than simply averting death.' And Lord Justice Hoffmann pointed out that 'the resources of the National Health Service are not limitless and choices have to be made... one is bound to observe that the cost of keeping a patient like Anthony Bland alive is very considerable and that in another case the health authority might conclude that its resources were better devoted to other patients.'[10]

Subsequent cases have shown how quickly the law can slide in this area; and we have noted (at 12.4.4) the BMA's recent (1999) guidance to doctors on withdrawing food and water delivered by tube, in addition to medical treatment, from a wide-ranging group of patients who have suffered severe mental impairment. Perhaps alarmed already by this trend, the House of Lords, in the Select Committee established in the wake of the Bland judgment, noted (in 1994) that 'despite the inevitable continuing constraints on healthcare resources' there is a 'compelling social responsibility to care adequately for those who are elderly, dying or disabled'. 'Such a responsibility,' the Lords observed, 'is costly to discharge, but is not one which we can afford to neglect.'[11] Any treatment-limiting decisions should be made on the basis of therapeutic appropriateness 'and should not be determined by considerations of resource availability.'[12] 'Long-term care of those whose disability or dementia makes them dependent should have special regard to the need to maintain the dignity of the individual to the highest possible degree.'[13]

With all of this we are in full agreement. Any society as affluent as ours cannot justify abandonment of frail elderly, handicapped, chronic or poor patients on financial grounds. But the now well-established tendency in the NHS to discriminate against the frail elderly has clearly been given a semblance of legitimacy in the eyes of some by the approval of the Courts for withholding tubefeeding from those with the poorest 'quality of life', the irreversibly unconscious. A coherent attempt to reverse this tendency should begin with legislative reversal of the judgements in *Bland* (see 16.3 below).[14]

Part V

Catholic Social Teaching

15

Catholic social teaching and the allocation of healthcare

The foregoing chapters, in the interests of promoting common understanding, all appeal to reasoned considerations the force of which may be recognised without benefit of Christian faith. But Christian faith itself gives powerful support to those considerations. This is because answers to questions about healthcare resource allocation must make underlying assumptions about the nature and dignity of the human person, and about the nature of human community and how people should relate to each other. Catholic Christianity has a developed body of teaching about these fundamental matters as well as about the ethics of healthcare. A fully adequate understanding of the human situation and of the truths we need to grasp if we are to live well is available to us only in virtue of revelation and, in particular, of our revealed knowledge of human destiny. So this chapter sets the main elements of the moral framework developed in previous chapters within the broader context of understanding provided by divine revelation.

15.1 Introduction

Much of this Report has been built upon 'common morality': those principles and approaches common to people of all religions and none, articulated in documents ranging from great religious texts to international human rights documents, and described by many thinkers both secular and religious. We have adopted points of departure, methods of argumentation, and language common to many outside our faith tradition in order better to provide an exposition which may appeal to, and engage in dialogue, people of all religions and none. We are confident that all human beings share a 'moral sense which enables them to discern by reason the good and the evil, the truth and the lie.'[1]

Nonetheless we believe that specifically Catholic thinking in this area has a unique contribution to make because of the strong association of the Church with healthcare, its centuries of accumulated experience and wisdom in dealing with healthcare dilemmas, and the particular gifts of inspiration, sensitivity and reason which it brings to bear on moral questions more generally. Healthcare allocation is a theological matter every bit as much as it is an issue for philosophy, medicine or public policy – for it goes to the heart of attitudes toward the dignity of the human person, the nature of community, and right relations between people under God.[2] Decisions about healthcare allocation have implications beyond the obvious ones for effective and efficient healthcare management: they contribute to or hinder a greater reality which, by virtue of God's promise and grace, can begin in this life and extend into the completed kingdom and family of God in heaven.[3]

Furthermore, while a sound ethic can in principle be recognised and lived by anyone of good will and right reason, reason's full implications, and morality's practical applications, are well understood only when full account is taken of the human situation. Catholics believe that the human situation is only adequately and reliably illuminated by the life and teachings of Jesus Christ, mediated to us in the Church's Scriptures and tradition. A theologically-informed ethic thus assists the agent to live a 'fully human life' by educating conscience, shaping character, and facilitating wise choices in particular cases; it also helps people respond to their divine calling and prepares them for eternal life.[4]

Lastly, Catholic tradition offers an especially rich collection of resources in the areas of social ethics[5] and bioethics[6] – the very two areas which intersect in our present investigation. The following are among the points made repeatedly in the teaching on social ethics: the dignity of the human person; the consequent rights (reasonable expectations) of persons to those things necessary for their flourishing (including rights to life, food and shelter, healthcare and education, work and a worthy standard of living ...); the nature of persons as social and political animals who must co-operate to achieve their good; the consequent duties to respect civil rights, collaborate mutually, and act responsibly with respect to others; the intimate link between love and justice; the consequent special care for the poor and marginalized and opposition to attitudes such as racism; the notions of community, common good, needs, rights and duties as the context for the establishment of social, political and economic relations; and 'subsidiarity' or supportive decentralisation of decision-making and opportunities. In the official documents on Catholic bioethics, respect for the dignity of the human person is again emphasised, especially in the face of contemporary threats to human life and health even in healthcare situations. Nothing can lessen the intrinsic goodness and inviolability of human life; no personal or social benefit can justify its destruction or abandonment. These documents show an acute awareness of the very real pressures presently faced by health planners, healthworkers and patients, such as limited resources; but the Church remains committed to preaching 'the Gospel of Life' and to championing the cause of the victims of 'the culture of death', opposing all disrespectful, uncaring and especially homicidal healthcare decisions, including those made in the interests of 'more efficient' resource allocation.

15.2 The dignity of the human person and the right to live and flourish

Catholic reflection upon the appropriate level and allocation of healthcare begins with the claim that every human being has intrinsic, equal and inalienable dignity or worth, deserving uncompromising reverence and respect. Persons are created 'in the image of God' (Gen 1:26) as free and rational beings with a divine calling, and restored to that image by Christ's redemptive work (Eph 1:10; 1 Tim 2:46) making them children of God.[7] The Author and Lord of life commands reverence and love for every person. Their life and health are precious gifts – 'talents' – entrusted to human beings by God to be cherished and well used.[8] We have an inalienable responsibility to take reasonable care of our own health and that of our dependents, without selfishly ignoring the needs of others and the demands of the common good.[9] And because much healthcare is beyond our personal capacities to provide, we must co-operate with others if we are to fulfil this responsibility.[10] Above all, then, any healthcare system must be consistent with respect for and indeed positively serve 'the primary and absolute value of life: of all human life and the life of each and every human being'.[11]

Furthermore, as the Second Vatican Council noted,

> Human persons by their very nature stand completely in need of life in society ... Life in society is not something accessory to human persons: through their dealings with others, through mutual service, and through fraternal dialogue, people develop their talents and are enabled to rise to their destiny.[12]

Social by nature and grace, persons are bound together as a community by birth as 'children of the first Adam and the first Eve' and by redemption as 'children of the new Adam and the new Eve'. As members of one human family and the community of disciples, they are called to love one another and to collaborate in providing for the means for each other's proper development, especially where individuals cannot provide for their needs by themselves.[13] Opposing 'the luxury of a merely individualistic morality' Christians insist upon the obligations of justice and mercy which are only satisfied by contributing to the common good according to one's means and the needs of others.[14] Their love is to exceed the ordinary limitations of affection, overcome the hopelessness evoked by the enormity of some social problems, and the partiality, indifference and individualism common in the face of competing interests. As Vatican Council II declared:

> Everyone should look upon their neighbour (without exception) as another self, bearing in mind above all the neighbour's life and the means necessary for living it in a dignified way (Jas 2:15–16) lest he follow the example of the rich man who ignored Lazarus, the poor man (Lk 16:19–31).[15]

Thus the impetus behind Christian healthcare down through the ages has been a high regard for the human person and a concern to love one's neighbour as oneself (Mt 19:19), spending oneself for them (Mt cc. 5 and 6; Jn 13:34; 15:13), thereby seeking first God's Kingdom and trying to be like him (Mt 5:48; 6:33). The model of this self-sacrificing love is, of course, Jesus, who 'went about doing good and healing everyone' (Acts 10:38).[16] Care for the sick and the weak, the suffering and the sinful, was a major focus of his life and served alongside his words and mighty deeds to proclaim the coming of God's kingdom.

He restored sight to the blind (Mk 8:22–26; 10:46–52; Mt 20: 29–34), hearing to the deaf (Mk 7:32–37; Mt 11:5) and speech to the mute (Mt 9:32–33; 12:22; Lk 11:14). He cured the woman with a haemorrhage (Mk 5:25–34), lepers (Mk 1:40–45; Lk 17:12–19) and the paralysed and lame (Mk 2:3–12; Mt 8:6–13; 21:14; Jn 5: 3–8). He even restored dead people to life (Mk 5:35–43; Lk 7:12–17; Jn 11; cf. Mk 9:17–29). For Mark Jesus is very much the exorcist-healer. Luke records that in initiating his ministry, Jesus declared programmatically that he had been anointed not only to bring good news to the poor but also sight to the blind (Lk 4:17) and that he later compared himself with a physician (of bodies and souls: Lk 5:31), with a miraculous preacher-healer (Lk 7:22–23), and with a Good Samaritan nursing a Jew mugged and left for dead (Lk 10:29–37). His many cures are summed up by Luke (14:40): 'Now when the sun was setting, all those who had any sick with various diseases brought them to him; and he laid his hands on them and healed them.' Likewise Matthew (15:30–31; cf. Mk 7:37) tells us: 'Great crowds came to him, bringing with them the lame, the maimed, the blind, the mute, and many others. They put them at his feet, and he cured them, so that the crowd were amazed when they saw the mute speaking, the maimed whole, the lame walking, and the blind seeing. And they praised the God of Israel.' Indeed, so replete was his life with the cure of every kind of ailment and disease (Mt 9:35) that Matthew interpreted Jesus' mission as the fulfilment of the prophecy of Isaiah: 'He took away our infirmities and bore our diseases' (Mt 8:17; cf. Is 53:4).[17]

At Christ's own invitation, Christians are to see in every suffering person a brother or sister in need, indeed Christ himself, and know that what they do for this person they do also for Christ and for Christ's sake (Mt 25:31–40).[18]

In faithful imitation and continuation of that ministry, Christians have served the sick, suffering and dying in various ways throughout history: monastic pharmacies and infirmaries; hospitals, nursing homes, hospices for the dying, and medical and nurse training schools run by religious orders; lay faithful committed to healthcare as their vocation; sacramental and other pastoral care for the sick; systematic reflection on healthcare ethics. Modeling their efforts on Jesus' own work, these men and women have demonstrated the power of healthcare as an authentic expression of neighbourliness toward those in need.[19]

> The mystery of Christ casts light on every facet of Catholic health care: to see Christian love as the animating principle of health care; to see healing and compassion as a continuation of Christ's mission; to see suffering as a participation in the redemptive power of Christ's passion, death and resurrection; and to see death, transformed by the resurrection, as an opportunity for a final act of communion with Christ.[20]

Here, as elsewhere, Christians have opposed unjust discrimination,[21] and have sought to make healthcare an integral part of the Church's mission to preach and live the Gospel.[22]

Health is not, however, an exclusive, dominant value[23] or healthcare the only good goal of persons; nor are life, health and resources infinite.[24] Pain and death will not be eliminated in this life. Suffering must be faced head-on, against the pervasive temptation of contemporary secular societies to demand an immediate technological 'fix' for every discomfort and to devote endless resources to the futile quest to extend life indefinitely or to achieve perfect health and comfort throughout life. Part of the specifically Christian contribution to consideration of what is appropriate in healthcare will therefore be reflection upon the meaning of sickness and death and the human encounter with both in healthcare situations.[25] Christians believe that suffering can be united to the Redeemer's cross (Col 1:24) and so share in its salvific efficacy.

> On the Cross, the miracle of the serpent lifted up by Moses in the desert (Jn 3:14–15; cf. Num 21:8–9) is renewed and brought to full and definitive perfection. Today, too, by looking upon the one who was pierced, every person whose life is threatened encounters the sure hope of finding freedom and redemption.[26]

Thus without in any way minimizing or exaggerating the reality of human suffering, they acknowledge it not with blind resignation but with the serene knowledge that the human spirit under grace can triumph even over sickness, pain and death and that God can bring good out of any evil.[27] The limitations of healthcare and of health resources are, therefore, no ultimate tragedy, but merely the field in which people of good will are called to do all that is practically and morally possible under grace, entrusting the rest to the God of love.

15.3 The right to healthcare

In addition to being a manifestation of Christian love and concern for suffering others, healthcare has been viewed by the Christian tradition as an entitlement in justice – but under a view of justice which is about right relations between persons and an imaginative, generous, merciful application of the Golden Rule (Mt 7:12), rather than the narrow contractual conception all too common today.[28] The right of individuals to live and to flourish, and the duty of communities to assist their members in achieving these goals, are the foundations of the Catholic claim that there is a right to healthcare.

Thus Pope John XXIII taught in *Pacem in Terris*:

> Man has a right to live. He has the right to bodily integrity and to the means necessary for the proper development of life, particularly food, clothing, shelter, medical care, rest, and finally, the necessary social services. In consequence, he has the right to be looked after in the event of ill-health, disability [and] old age.[29]

Similarly, John Paul II has said that 'as regards necessities – food, clothes, housing, medical and social assistance... – there must be no privileged social strata',[30] for every individual has a 'primary right... to what is necessary for the care of his health and therefore to adequate health services'. The *Catechism of the Catholic Church* echoes these sentiments, insisting that communities must provide the conditions for the well-being and development of their members, including access to adequate healthcare.[31] The US Bishops have argued that

> Every person has a basic right to adequate healthcare. This right flows from the sanctity of human life and the dignity that belongs to all human persons, who are made in the image of God. It implies that access to that healthcare which is necessary and suitable for proper development and maintenance of life must be provided for all people, regardless of

economic, social, or legal status. Special care should be given to meeting the basic health needs of the poor.[32]

15.4 The option for the poor and sick

Catholic reflection upon the duty of communities to provide adequate healthcare to their members is further enriched by the social doctrine of the 'option' or 'preferential love' of God and his Church for the poor, sick and otherwise disadvantaged.[33] This doctrine has a long history, stretching back well into the Old Testament period. The prophets, for instance, commonly focussed their critical gaze upon idolatry of various kinds – not just of foreign gods, but of wealth, power and privilege – and upon the quality of relationships between individuals, between communities, and with God. They preached *hesed* (love or mercy) and *sedekah* (justice, or righteousness), which included harmonious community life, distributive justice, honesty and fair dealing. The litmus test of this mercy and justice was how the *anawim* (widows, orphans, the poor, refugees...) were treated; the prophets spoke for God in condemning the predatory rich and powerful for their oppression or hard-heartedness towards the deprived.

Jesus took up this notion himself, teaching his disciples to be compassionate to all (as is their heavenly Father: Lk 6:36) but especially to the 'marginalised'. His parable of the feast of the kingdom of God began with the instruction: 'When you hold a banquet, invite the poor, the crippled, the lame, the blind' (Lk 14:13)[34] and these were the very sorts of people whom Jesus most often healed and associated with. It was by how each of us treats the least advantaged that he proposed to judge us (Mt 25:40).[35]

The Fathers of the Church and its great scholastic Doctors echoed Christ's words in their 'radical' claims that 'not to share with the poor is to steal from them, indeed to kill them' whereas 'to attend to their needs is to give them what is rightly theirs, not ours'.[36] This ancient theme has been restated and amplified in various ways in modern Catholic social teaching dating from Pope Leo XIII (*Rerum novarum* 1892).

The so-called 'preferential option for the poor' is a counsel of justice perfected by Christian mercy, and applies as much to healthcare allocation as elsewhere in life. Thus Christians themselves, individually or co-operating as charitable organizations, have established healthcare institutions and programmes targeted at the poor and otherwise disadvantaged; and they have also sought to ensure the social conditions, including government programmes, necessary to complement these efforts if those who cannot provide for themselves are to be guaranteed access to adequate healthcare. The US Bishops observed a few years ago that:

> In accord with its mission, Catholic healthcare should distinguish itself by service to and advocacy for those people whose social condition puts them at the margins of our society and makes them particularly vulnerable to discrimination: the poor, the uninsured and the underinsured; children, the unborn, single parents and the elderly; those with incurable diseases and chemical dependencies; and racial minorities, immigrants and refugees. In particular, the person with mental or physical disabilities, regardless of the cause or severity, must be treated as a unique person of incomparable worth, with the same right to life and to adequate healthcare as all other persons.[37]

If traditional distributions of healthcare or contemporary trends in allocation further disadvantage such people – and put their health and very lives at risk – the Catholic community can be expected to oppose such distributions and seek reform. And their own healthcare institutions must give a lead in this respect.

A growing and increasingly disadvantaged group which the Catholic Church has been especially keen in recent times to commend to the attention of those who distribute health resources has been the elderly[38] – a group for whom 'filial piety' would commend special consideration in any case.[39] In *Evangelium Vitae* Pope John Paul renewed this call, pointing to the danger in cultures such as ours that the elderly will be regarded as 'a useless burden' and consequently abandoned or even killed. In place of such 'intolerable' neglect of the elderly, he exhorts us to reestablish a sort of 'covenant' between generations in which there is mutual respect and support of various kinds – including, of course, healthcare.[40]

15.5 The responsibility of the community to respond to healthcare needs

The sources of communal responsibility for healthcare are thus several: reverence for the goodness of life and health not only as experienced by ourselves but by all others; our nature as social beings, interdependent by nature and called by grace to the service of others; the obligation to express such care and respect in concrete acts such as the provision of healthcare; the need for the community's contribution towards, and participation in, healthcare to be large-scale if it is to be achieved at the level which can reasonably be expected in the contemporary world; the natural expectation on the part of members of a community that such assistance will be available to them in order that they might live, flourish and participate in the life of their society; and the particular concern of Christians that the most disadvantaged as 'God's little ones' be given special care. As the *Catechism of the Catholic Church* observes:

> On coming into the world, man is not equipped with every-thing he needs for developing his bodily and spiritual life. He needs others. Differences appear tied to age, physical abilities, intellectual or moral aptitudes, the benefits derived from social commerce, and the distribution of wealth. These 'talents' are not distributed equally. These differences belong to God's plan, who wills that each receive what he needs from others, and that those endowed with particular 'talents' share the benefits with those who need them. These differences encourage and often oblige persons to practise generosity, kindness and sharing of goods; they foster mutual enrichment...[41]

Two fundamental ideas here are 'the common good' and 'distributive justice'. The common good is described variously in Catholic social teaching as the range of economic, political and social conditions necessary for the flourishing of individual members of a community, for respect for fundamental rights, and/or for achieving appropriate common goals.[42] Co-responsibility for the common good – 'love of neighbour' or 'solidarity' – is the basis of the duties to pay taxes,[43] to show loyalty to the group and respect for its authority,[44] to show respect for human rights,[45] to co-operate to provide the necessities for the flourishing of all,[46] to seek (only reasonable) assistance from the community with respect to achieving one's own fulfilment. It requires fellow-feeling, genuine self-giving, joint effort with others to promote the flourishing of all, encouragement and support for the efforts of others, and various interventions by the state in accordance with a just hierarchy of values.

The provision of healthcare, whether by individual health professionals[47] or by the community as a whole,[48] is an expression of this virtue of solidarity. And people have an ethical claim on the community in general, and the health professions in particular, for help in the maintenance of their health. This is, in the Christian view of things, part of what society is for and a large part of what (private) property and (medical) education are for. But it has its limits: we have no right to expect that everyone else go without so that we can have the best of everything.

We have examined secular conceptions of distributive justice in previous chapters. In chapter 11 (11.4) we proposed that distributive justice in healthcare might be judged by a test something like this: *would I think the healthcare budget and its distribution was fair if I (or someone I loved) were in healthcare need, especially if I were among the weakest in the community (i.e. sick with a chronic, disabling and expensive ailment, elderly, poor and illiterate)? Would I think it were fair if I were one who would go without under the proposed arrangements?* This approach is strongly supported by Jesus' own enunciation of the Golden Rule (Mt 7:12),[49] his explication of its radical demands in the Sermon on the Mount (e.g. Mt 5:40–42; 6:2–4; cf. 10:8), and his repeated insistence on the duties of those with power and wealth to redistribute to the poor and to see things from their perspective (e.g. Mt 19:23–26; Lk 6:24; 12:16–21; 16:19–31).[50] Jesus' is certainly a much richer conception of justice than those 'liberal' accounts we analysed in chapters 7 and 8.

15.6 The limits to autonomy in property ownership and healthcare

Implicit in the claim that the community has duties to provide a certain level of healthcare, especially to those unable to provide for themselves, is a limit to the rights of private property: otherwise no-one would be morally required to give up what is 'theirs' by paying just taxes or by appropriate 'charitable' donations. Catholic teaching upholds the usefulness of private ownership but insists upon the universal destination of the goods of the earth (i.e. that the world's resources were created for the flourishing of all) and the consequent duty of those who 'have' to share with those who 'have-not'. This puts it very much at odds with liberal ideologies which absolutize private property, talents and energies, and the right to dispose of these benefits as one wishes. As Vatican II declared:

> In their use of things people should regard the external goods they legitimately own not merely as exclusive to themselves but common to others also, in the sense that they can benefit others as well as themselves. Therefore everyone has the right to possess a sufficient amount of the earth's goods for themselves and their family. This has been the opinion of the Fathers and Doctors of the Church, who taught that people are bound to come to the aid of the poor and to do so not merely out of their superfluous goods.[51]

Against the background of this traditional teaching, the Church has criticized 'excessive economic and social disparities' between individuals and societies as 'a source of scandal' which also 'militates against social justice, equity, human dignity, as well as peace'[52] and called for 'every effort to be made to put an end as soon as possible to these immense inequalities'.[53] Instead of a view of property as a thing to be accumulated, profited from, used and disposed of as the owner wishes, the Christian tradition promotes the notion of 'responsible stewardship' for the goods of creation, circumscribed by proper commitments (e.g. to one's own family or patients), the needs of particular others, and the requirements of the common good.[54] Recent Catholic social teaching has been especially critical of the risks of avarice, acquisitiveness and waste in consumerist societies, the indifference of many affluent people toward the poor, and the swing of governments away from redistributive taxation, welfare 'safety nets', and foreign aid to poor nations, towards a kind of 'economic rationalism' which encourages and enacts hard-heartedness and selfishness.

Healthcare resources are like all other goods in this respect: those with access to or control of them have duties of responsible steward-ship over them, ensuring that such resources are not squandered uselessly nor hoarded meanly, and that they are distributed justly and efficiently with respect for each person's needs and the good health of all the community.[55] The Church has consistently called for a redistribution of medical resources from the richer to the poorer, both within and between societies,[56] and for an 'integrated and comprehensive' view of public health and healthcare which encourages not only cure but prevention also.[57]

15.7 The principle of subsidiarity

'Subsidiarity' is a word which had some currency in the political rhetoric of the 1980s. As a principle of Catholic social teaching it means that each should be encouraged, enabled and willing to take responsibility for their own sphere (for themselves, their dependents...) and be given assistance (*subsidium*) to do so, rather than having that responsibility taken over by individuals and groups with greater power and resources. This doctrine favours a 'decentralisation' of decisionmaking and resource allocation, with governments and other larger or more powerful groups avoiding usurping such functions where they can be adequately achieved by individuals and smaller and less powerful associations.[58] Pope John Paul II articulates the principle thus:

> A community of a higher order should not interfere in the internal life of a community of a lower order, depriving the latter of its functions, but rather should support it in case of need and help co-ordinate its activity with the activities of the rest of society, always with a view to the common good.[59]

Applied to healthcare allocation this doctrine suggests that larger units (such as central government) ought not to assume functions that smaller units (such as health authorities, primary care groups, charities, individual healthworkers or, most importantly, patients themselves) could effectively perform. In chapter 16 we shall see that recent NHS reforms have sometimes been attributed, at least in part, to this principle. Whether a commitment to subsidiarity is really behind these moves is debateable, but it might represent a useful corrective to any previous tendencies to undue paternalism, authoritarianism, or unnecessary centralisation. Two points should be noted about the application of the principle of subsidiarity: first that recent changes have been accompanied by the growth of an increasingly large and complex health bureaucracy; and secondly, that the principle should not be invoked by larger, more powerful and better resourced bodies, such as central government, as a reason for withdrawing from responsibility (e.g. devolving responsibility for care of the elderly to local councils or to families) where the smaller, less powerful and poorer unit cannot adequately fulfill this responsibility or is not being resourced to do so.

15.8 The model of the Good Samaritan

After criticizing a number of long-established and contemporary approaches to healthcare allocation (chapters 5 to 8) we proposed a more substantive, 'natural law' alternative which attends more adequately to the goods of the human person and community, and to the norms and virtues which follow therefrom (chapters 9 to 11). On this basis we argued that a just health service will (as far as possible) ensure access for all members of the community to care sufficient to meet their healthcare needs; and we specified what this level and these needs may be. We suggested some ways in which needs may be identified, moderated, sorted and reasonably satisfied. We argued further (in chapters 12 to 13) that healthcare should be allocated according to need, irrespective of factors such as race, religion, social contribution, age, consciousness, intelligence, quality of life, provider-whim and ability to pay. We noted a possible exception to a strictly needs-egalitarian approach: preference in favour of the disadvantaged, a choice which would be supported by the Catholic social doctrine elaborated in 15.4, the 'option for the poor'.

At several points in the present Report we have suggested that the Gospel parable of the Good Samaritan (Lk 10:25–37) is a useful model for good practice in healthcare allocation. The Good Samaritan is the story of one person's ready response to the suffering of another human being before him; it tells of the recognition of claims which rest on our common humanity, of the character of the virtuous person, of the 'common humanitarian duty of care' and, particularly, of the norm that one ought (where possible and reasonable) to assist 'neighbours' who are gravely and immediately in need of care. It is a model of human relating which, while manifestly concerned with practicalities – the Samaritan intervenes to provide very practical assistance, seeks help from others (the inn-keeper) to do so, and ensures that the latter is justly paid – does not reduce such relationships to utilitarian transactions, to be assessed in the light of cost-benefit considerations. It is a story, above all, of rescue and inclusiveness: God's rescue of damaged, abandoned, desperate humankind; Christ the Physician, healer of bodies and souls, responding to crying need wherever it is heard; and the Christian imitating this, participating in God's continuing work of rescue and inclusion, and responding to Christ's command to 'Go and do likewise' (Lk 10:37). As awareness of needs and ability to assist increase, so do the scope and opportunities for good neighbourliness: as the Second Vatican Council suggested, 'today there is an inescapable duty to make ourselves the neighbour of every person, no matter who they are, and if we meet them, to come to their aid in a positive way'.[60]

The Good Samaritan parable has long inspired the vocation of Christian healthcare: the response to a transcendent call to care lovingly for the sick person, to treat all those in need of such care, and to do one's best to save, heal and care.[61] Only the consciousness of such a divine 'calling' or 'mission' 'can motivate and sustain the most disinterested, available and faithful commitment' of health-workers, and it is this that gives their work a saving, 'priestly' value.[62]

The Good Samaritan model of rescue and inclusiveness stands in stark contrast to certain alternative bases for healthcare allocation which we have examined in this Report: discrimination against certain patients on the basis of undesired characteristics (the Samaritan's unlikely patient was a Jew for whom Samaritans were aliens); preference on the basis of social contribution or ability to pay (the Samaritan does not inquire into these); punishment for self-destructive behaviour (he likewise does not ask whether the victim 'brought it upon himself'); or QALY maximisation (we cannot imagine the Good Samaritan assessing whether the man beaten and left for dead will derive enough quality-adjusted life-years to justify the investment of two healthcare denarii).

In chapter 11 we proposed that health systems, like the Good Samaritan's acts of rescue and care, can be symbolic demonstrations of crucial values, such as generosity, respect for the dignity and equality of persons, for the inviolability of human life and the good of health, special concern for the vulnerable and powerless, solidarity with and compassion for those who suffer. 'Every society's judgments and conduct' – including its healthcare allocations – 'reflect a vision of the human person and their destiny.'[63] Thus health systems can tell the story of the kind of people we are and wish to be.

The Good Samaritan model does *not* counsel that we should give all our attention or spend all our resources on any one case of need. Indeed while the compassionate Samaritan delays his travels so as to care for the beaten and abandoned stranger, he then hands him over to an inn-keeper and continues his own work, promising to make good the hospitaler's expenses on his return. The rescuer, then, has other responsibilities too, and these properly make their demands on his or her time and resources. Nor is the Good Samaritan the only model offered us by Christ: the wise steward is also praised

(Mt 24:45; cf. Mt 10:16; 25:1–13; 25:14–30) and preventative health-care strategies – no part of the Good Samaritan's work – are increasingly commended by the Church.[64] Thus Christians are recommended to combine the roles of both merciful healer and wily steward.

15.9 Conclusion

As citizens Christians are obliged to take an active part in public affairs, promoting social goods such as: civil and economic justice – often a powerful determinant of health; respect, protection and promotion of basic human goods – including life and health; and access to appropriate social assistance – including healthcare. To achieve this they have various responsibilities: to vote conscientiously – taking into account the attitude of candidates to the fundamental requirements of justice (and most particularly the absolute prohibition on killing the innocent) as well as their attitude to specific health policies; to obey just laws and pay just taxes – thereby contributing to a good health service, among other things; to make no unreasonable demands of government and society – including immoderate claims upon the health service; to contribute personally and to associate with others in complementing any government programmes to promote human flourishing – by, for instance, contributing to Church and other charity hospitals; and (sometimes) to participate more actively in politics – e.g. lobbying for the basic requirements of justice and for good health policies, or even standing for election with a view to securing justice in the practice of healthcare.

Many of the principles proposed to us in Catholic social and bioethical teaching, and which we have outlined in this chapter, provide only general orientations and bases for criticism, rather than specific directions on the best allocative mechanisms and healthcare programmes. Within these confines there may be legitimate differences between communities and between individuals over such things as: the extent to which access to provision for needs is a right; the proportion of a nation's national income which should be given over to healthcare as compared to other worthwhile purposes; the best balance between government, the market and the individual in healthcare provision; the appropriate response to particular kinds and cases of sickness; and the very urgency of healthcare rationing. Catholic teaching allows room both for the objective, universal requirements of the moral law and a range of culturally particular responses to the demands of that law. Above all it calls individuals and communities to conversion and to a genuinely Christian life, without which the virtues necessary for meeting healthcare needs are hardly likely to flourish.

Part VI

Conclusion

16

Implications for public policy

This chapter discusses the implications of the moral framework we have advanced for some questions of public policy: how much money should be spent on healthcare? Should there be legislative recognition of a right to healthcare? Is any other legislation required given facts about identifiable injustices in healthcare practice? What considerations should govern the allocation of funding for healthcare? What considerations should govern our response to proposals for the kind of mix that should obtain between private and NHS provision of healthcare? Who should make the allocation decisions? And why is public debate needed?

16.1 How much should be spent on healthcare?

On the basis of the considerations we have advanced, it is clear that healthcare spending should be sufficient to ensure access for all to a level of healthcare adequate to satisfy their genuine needs within a reasonable time and without unreasonable disincentives. This requires availability of 'services that are sufficiently comprehensive to promote good health, to provide adequate treatment for persons with disease and disability, and to care for persons who are chronically ill or dying'.[1] This will at least include the provision of basic public health measures, primary care, emergency services, and hospital-based services of proven value.[2] If there are dangerously long queues, or some people have no access to basic services, or the standard of care is unsatisfactory to the majority of people, or a large proportion of the community seeks to 'buy out' of or otherwise circumvent the healthcare system available to ordinary people, this may well indicate that the system is inadequate.

In assessing total healthcare needs there will be a dialectic between the various levels of provision outlined in 1.5: thus, for instance, a government may choose to increase total healthcare spending if, after experience and reflection, it seems that the services which can reasonably be provided within the given budget are inadequate; or it may choose to redistribute or even rein back health spending where it has been found to be inefficient or ineffective in achieving the goals suggested above. This sensitivity and responsiveness should apply at each level of budget allocation from national and regional to local and between departments and even between physicians within institutions: at each level the allocating agency should have both adequate information coming 'from below' on healthcare need and adequate resources coming 'from above' to meet those needs until some sort of equilibrium is reached, with the allocation at each level satisfying the claims of justice and not just of economics.

Judged by these standards, the ideals of the NHS from its inception – universality and comprehensiveness of access, irrespective of factors other than medical need – are fundamentally sound and deserve support; and historically there has been a not inconsiderable measure of success in the implementation of these ideals. As we have seen, however, there has recently been concern about the sustainability of these goals. Any community must seek to satisfy such worthwhile objectives in the context of (a) the resource and opportunity costs of attempting to achieve them, (b) its available resources, and (c) the competing goals of that community.

In chapter 10 we suggested some ways in which needs can and should be moderated, and in chapter 13 how they can be sorted. It remains that the satisfaction of needs is likely to make very considerable demands upon a community's resources, and that some people will be denied potentially beneficial services in even the most moderate, just and generous of communities. *There is no simple algorithm for deciding among the various good uses to which a community can put its resources; there is no one right answer, though there are a number of mistaken approaches to finding answers.* Some have looked to historical levels of or trends in spending, or amounts spent on equally or less important things, or spending levels or trends in comparable countries.[3] But while these levels and trends may indicate what is socio-economically or politically sustainable or what are the expectations within a community of nations at a particular time, they are not of themselves conclusively normative. Different societies will appropriately develop in different directions and judge their spending priorities according to local traditions, debates and political processes – though these must in turn be subject to moral criticism.

This much can, however, be said about any society's decision about what priority to give healthcare spending relative to other worthy goals. On the one hand, health and healthcare are not 'supergoods' always trumping all others: there are other worthy social goals which should not be neglected. On the other hand, because spending levels or allocation systems or policies which fall short of satisfying all healthcare needs can imperil the life or health of individuals, they require strong ethical justification. Reasonable steps must have been taken to eliminate inefficiencies and waste such as unnecessary administrative costs, excessive profit margins, ethically and medically inappropriate treatments, and tests and treatments of only marginal benefit. Steps should also be taken to ensure that taxpayers make reasonable sacrifices for such a great social good.

16.2 Should a right to healthcare be recognized?

A number of international instruments – to some of which the UK is a party – assert a right to healthcare. The *Universal Declaration of Human Rights* (1948) declares that 'everyone has the right to a standard of living adequate for the health and well-being of self and family, including... medical care and necessary social services' (§ 25). The *International Covenant on Economic, Social and Cultural Rights* (1966) asserts 'the right of everyone to the enjoyment of the highest attainable standard of physical and mental health' including 'the creation of conditions which would assure to all medical service and medical attention in the event of sickness' (§ 12). This right is to be government-guaranteed and 'no discrimination of any kind' allowed 'as to race, colour, sex, language, religion, political or other opinion, national or social origin, property, birth or other status' (§ 2.2). Similarly the preamble to the *Constitution of the World Health Organization* states that 'the enjoyment of the highest attainable standard of health is one of the fundamental rights of every human being without distinction of race, religion, political belief, economic or social condition'. And the *Bioethics Convention of the Council of Europe* provides that: 'Parties shall take appropriate measures with a view to providing, within their jurisdiction, equitable access to healthcare, taking into account the health needs and available resources' (§ 4).

Whatever the aspirations of these international charters, and their growing authority in international and local law, few countries have moved to include a right to healthcare in their constitutions or local legislation. The National Health Service Act 1977 and *mutatis mutandis* its Scots equivalent provide:

> 1(1) It is the Secretary of State's duty to continue the promotion in England and Wales of a comprehensive health service designed to secure improvement (a) in the physical and mental health of the people of those countries, and (b) in the prevention, diagnosis and treatment of illness, and to provide or secure the effective provision of services in accordance with this Act...

> 3(1) It is the Secretary of State's duty to provide throughout England and Wales, to such extent as he considers necessary to meet all reasonable requirements – (a) hospital accommodation; (b) other accommodation for the purpose of any service provided under this Act; (c) medical, dental, nursing and ambulance services; (d) such other facilities for the care of expectant mothers and young children as he considers are appropriate as part of the health service; (e) such facilities for the prevention of illness and the aftercare of persons who have suffered from illness as he considers are appropriate as part of the health service; (f) such other services as are required for the diagnosis and treatment of illness.

These duties are to some extent delegated to the health authorities.

Do these duties amount to a justiciable 'right to healthcare'? *Prima facie* they would seem to imply such a right and to ground causes in judicial review (an action against a public authority) where persons are denied necessary healthcare. However in *Hincks' Case* (1980) the complainants alleged that the Crown had failed to allocate the funds necessary to build an orthopaedic unit in Birmingham, and as a result they had waited an unreasonably long time – several years – for hip replacements. Bridge LJ noted that

> as we all know as a matter of common knowledge, the health service currently falls far short of what everyone would regard as the optimum desirable standard. This is very largely a situation brought about by lack of resources, lack of suitable equipment, lack of suitably qualified personnel, and above all lack of adequate finance.[4]

The Court of Appeal nonetheless held that there was no breach of statutory duty because the Act only imposes on the Secretary of State a duty to provide medical services 'to such extent as *he* considers necessary to meet all reasonable requirements'. Furthermore, this duty is properly confined by the government's budgetary decisions.

Likewise in *Walker's Case* (1987) the plaintiff alleged that her baby had been denied necessary surgical care because district health authorities had understaffed neonatal intensive care units. Sir John Donaldson MR held that 'it is not for this court, or indeed any court, to substitute its own judgment for the judgment of those who are responsible for the allocation of resources.' In the absence of wholly unreasonable behaviour,[5] any intervention by the court would simply tend to divert facilities from one patient to another.[6] The point was reiterated by Leggatt LJ in *Re J* (1992):

> I would stress the absolute undesirability of the court making an order which may have the effect of compelling a doctor or health authority to make available scarce resources (both human and material) to a particular child, without knowing whether or not there are other patients to whom those resources might more advantageously be devoted.

In this case the Court of Appeal set aside an order requiring a hospital intensively to resuscitate a handicapped child should this become necessary. The Master of the Rolls held that the order did not 'adequately take account of the sad fact that health authorities may, on occasion, find that they have too few resources, either human, material, or both, to treat all the patients whom they would like to treat in the way in which they would like to treat them. It is then their duty to make choices.' The Court was not willing to tie the hands of those responsible when such a choice became necessary; nor did it offer any guidance on how such a choice should be made.[7]

The question recurred in *Collier's Case* (1988). Brown LJ said, 'The courts of this country cannot arrange the lists in the hospitals, and, if there is no evidence that they are not being arranged properly due to some unreasonableness . . . the courts cannot, and should not, be asked to intervene.' Ralph-Gibson LJ held that the courts 'have no rôle of general investigator of social policy or of allocation of resources.'[8]

One case in which a judge *did* overturn a health authority's refusal to fund a treatment was the *Child B Case* (1995).[9] Child B was a 10-year old girl suffering from acute myeloid leukemia. After chemotherapy and a bone-marrow transplant her disease went into remission, but she later suffered a relapse. Her doctors felt that B should receive only palliative treatment but her father received other medical opinions supporting further treatment. The father requested the health authority to fund further chemotherapy (which would have only a 10–20% chance of success and would cost £15,000) and another bone marrow transplant (which would also have only a 10–20% chance of success and would cost £60,000). The authority refused, and the father sought judicial review.

Laws J quashed the authority's decision on the ground *inter alia* that 'where the question is whether the life of a 10-year-old child might be saved by however slim a chance, the responsible authority ... must do more than toll the bell of tight resources. They must explain the priorities that have led them to decline that treatment'.[10] However, the Court of Appeal disagreed with the judge's reasons and reversed his decision. Sir Thomas Bingham MR observed that the courts should confine themselves strictly to judging the lawfulness of allocation decisions, not their merits.[11] He added:

> Difficult and agonising judgements have to be made as to how a limited budget is best allocated to the maximum advantage of the maximum number of patients. That is not a judgement which the court can make.[12]

He also thought it would be 'totally unrealistic' to require the authority to come to court with its accounts to demonstrate that if further treatment were given to B, another patient would have to go without treatment.[13]

More recently, however, the Court of Appeal upheld a challenge to an authority's refusal of funding. *North West Lancashire Health Authority* v *A, D, & G* (1999)[14] concerned three transsexuals who wanted 'sex-change' operations. The authority's policy was to give low funding priority to procedures it considered of little or no clinical benefit. It would not fund 'gender reassignment' except in cases of 'overriding clinical need' or other exceptional circumstances, though it would fund psychotherapy. The authority refused requests by A, D, and G for funding to pay for referral to a specialist clinic for diagnosis and gender reassignment, despite the fact that psychiatrists supported their suitability. A, D, and G sought judicial review. Hidden J quashed the authority's refusal as *Wednesbury* unreasonable.[15] His decision was affirmed by the Court of Appeal.

Auld LJ said it was natural that a health authority, in discharging its duty under section 1 of the National Health Services Act 1977, would give greater priority to life-threatening and other grave illnesses. A policy of giving lower priority to gender reassignment and of denying it save in exceptional circumstances was not irrational, provided that the policy genuinely recognised the possibility of there being overriding clinical need and required each request to be considered on its merits. In establishing priorities, he added, it was vital for an authority accurately to assess the nature and seriousness of each type of illness; the effectiveness of various treatments; and to give proper weight to that assessment in the formulation and application of its policy.

Despite the authority's admission to the courts that transsexualism was an illness, other evidence, including its policy statements which bracketed it with cosmetic surgery, indicated that the authority did not really believe that it was. Consequently, its policy did not reflect its medical judgement. That 'basic error' was not mitigated by the exception for 'overriding clinical need' or other exceptional circumstances. Indeed, added Auld LJ, given the authority's reluctance to accept gender reassignment as an effective treatment for transsexualism, the exception was in practice meaningless. If an authority devised a policy not to provide treatment save in cases of overriding clinical need, it made nonsense of the policy if, as a matter of its medical judgement, there was no effective treatment.

In short, he held, given the authority's acknowledgement that transsexualism was an illness, its policy was flawed in two important respects. First, it did not in truth regard transsexualism as an illness, but as an attitude or state of mind which did not warrant medical treatment. Secondly, the ostensible provision it made for exceptions and its manner of considering them amounted to the operation of a 'blanket policy' against funding such treatment because it did not believe in such treatment. The authority should reformulate its policy to give proper weight to its acknowledgement that transsexualism was an illness and apply that weighting when setting its level of priority for treatment and make proper provision for exceptions in individual cases.

Buxton LJ pointed out that a health authority could still decide not to fund any treatment for a particular condition even if it were recognised as an illness requiring medical rather than cosmetic intervention.[16] There were, he added, many factors that this authority could properly take into account in reconsidering its refusal, such as

171

the cost of the procedure, the small number of patients needing the treatment, and the costs and demands of other treatments.[17]

Having dismissed the appeal on the basis of the common law, the court did not find it necessary to consider the respondents' submissions that the authority's refusal subjected them to 'inhuman and degrading treatment' contrary to Article 3 of the European Convention on Human Rights, and infringed their right to private and family life, contrary to Article 8, and amounted to sexual discrimination in breach of Council Directive 79/7/EEC and section 29 of the Sex Discrimination Act 1975. Indeed, the court regarded these 'unfocused' submissions as 'positively unhelpful, cluttering up its consideration of adequate and more precise domestic principles and authorities. . .'.[18] Buxton LJ observed that with the implementation of the Human Rights Act 1998, creating Convention rights in English law, it would be even more important that those rights were not inappropriately asserted. The respondents were awarded only two thirds of their costs.

This important case reaffirms that, subject to the supervisory jurisdiction of the courts, the discretion to allocate resources lies with health authorities. It provides an unusual example of a successful challenge to that discretion, reflecting a greater judicial willingness to scrutinise than has been evident in cases such as *Collier's Case* where the court declined even to seek the authority's reasons why the baby's life-saving heart operation had been postponed. Whether it presages more frequent recourse to the courts to resolve disputes about allocation decisions remains to be seen.

If there is presently no justiciable right to treatment, there are nonetheless legal entitlements once treatment has begun. Once a patient is *accepted* for treatment inadequacy of resources may be no defence regarding a failure to provide healthcare of a reasonable standard: a duty of care has arisen (and possibly a contractual duty) to satisfy current professional standards. In the *HIV Haemophiliac Case* (1990) Ralph-Gibson LJ again ruled: 'The fact that the decision attacked is made as a matter of discretion or policymaking does not make the decision immune in law. If it is *ultra vires* or wholly unreasonable the authority will be liable *in negligence* if the decision is shown to be negligent by reference to proximity and foreseeability.'[19] In *Wilsher's Case* (1987) Browne-Wilkinson VC held that 'a health authority which so conducts its hospital that it fails to provide doctors of sufficient skill and experience to give the treatment offered at the hospital may be directly liable in negligence to the patient'[20] and in *Bull's Case*

(1989) Mustill LJ held a health authority liable for failing to provide adequate protection for a mother and child in labour, even though the defendant pleaded limited resources and the common state of NHS hospitals.[21] Similarly Pill J ruled in *Knight's Case* (1989) that inadequate safety in a prison hospital was not to be excused by the lack of government funds.[22]

These cases seem to establish that, though patients lack recourse where treatment is not unreasonably denied them altogether due to resource allocation decisions, once treatment has begun management systems and resource shortages will not excuse substandard care. The failure of the courts to offer any guidance on how the internationally recognized and locally implied 'right to healthcare' should be specified or how health resources should be 'reasonably' distributed, has left citizens uncertain about their entitlements and health authorities and doctors uncertain about their legal responsibilities when allocating finite resources. On the other hand, British courts are likely to resist any trend in the direction of US malpractice suits, which have proven so productive of litigation, expense and defensive medicine. Anti-discrimination legislation in the UK and as enforced by the European courts may have increasing application to healthcare allocations. *But a case can be made for some clearer legislative recognition of a right to healthcare, which could ground proceedings before some tribunal where a person has been unjustly denied appropriate treatment.*

16.3 Other legislative action

Because of the substantial evidence, noted at various points in this Report, of unjust discrimination against the elderly, and particularly the cognitively impaired elderly, there is a strong case for specific legislation to outlaw such discrimination in the allocation of healthcare resources.

Prejudice against the cognitively impaired elderly is encouraged by the present state of the law following *Bland*. For *Bland* permits the withdrawal of tubefeeding of irreversibly unconscious patients precisely with the purpose of ending their lives. In other words, *Bland* permits euthanasia by deliberate omission, and what motivates the euthanasia is precisely the judgement that the patients' lives are no longer worthwhile. The present state of the law has encouraged the British Medical Association to recommend that doctors should be able to behave in a similar fashion towards patients with advanced dementia and those who have suffered severe brain damage as a result of stroke.[23] The BMA's *Guidance* proposes an extension of a radical form of discrimination against the severely cognitively impaired. It is of the first importance to remove the grounds in common law for such injustice. *There is therefore a need to reverse by legislation the Bland judgement.* The Government professes to be opposed to the legalisation of euthanasia while supporting the judgement in *Bland*. The two positions are not consistent and cannot be made consistent by the quite arbitrary stipulation that euthanasia can be carried out only by a positive act. Just as a parent, having a duty of care for his or her child, can be found guilty of murder for deliberately starving that child to death, so a doctor, having a duty of care for a patient, can certainly be morally guilty of murder for deliberately starving that patient to death and ought also to be reckoned guilty in law. Continued support for *Bland* can only encourage injustice to patients judged to have a poor quality of life, particularly the debilitated elderly.

16.4 How should the total sum allocated to healthcare be divided?

Having determined the total healthcare budget (hopefully in a flexible way which can respond to changing circumstances), and recognized in a general way the right of citizens to some basic level of healthcare, a community must establish some principles of distribution of limited resources. We have proposed that if allocation criteria are to be morally reasonable, they must accord with certain moral norms, virtues and values which properly guide and structure human choice.

First, we argued that certain negative norms, such as 'do not kill' and 'do not unjustly discriminate against persons', have specific implications for healthcare allocation, prohibiting, for instance, directly hastening the deaths of expensive or inconvenient patients, or establishing health policies or systems which encourage such behaviour, or allocating resources to immoral activities (such as abortion, in vitro fertilization, and cloning), or choosing between patients on the basis of skin colour, age and 'quality of life', or punitively withholding care.

Secondly, there is a range of positive norms with immediate relevance to distribution of healthcare such as 'preserve life', 'promote health', 'respect the dignity and equality of all others', 'seek the common good', 'follow the Golden Rule', 'help the weak', 'respect the freedom and conscience of others' and 'seek to achieve good ends by efficient (but not evil) means'. *We have argued that in our contemporary setting such norms would require allocating resources adequate for appropriate care of the elderly, the mentally ill, the handicapped, the newborn and the poor.*

A third requirement for a sound resolution of these problems is the cultivation of good character and attitudes. Particularly important in community life are attributes such as a strong sense of solidarity, fairness, impartiality, generosity and gratitude. If healthcare is to be financed and allocated justly, such virtues will have to be encouraged not just in healthworkers and planners, but in patients, tax-payers and voters. We also suggested that certain virtues such as courage and moderation among both healthworkers and patients will be crucial to restraining demand for health resources.

Fourthly, the allocation of healthcare will also properly be shaped by the hierarchy of values particular to that community and the mores appropriate to the health professions where these are not themselves unreasonable.

All this said, there will still be need for guiding principles or rules of thumb which direct choices between rival claims for limited healthcare resources. For this reason we examined several different criteria which have commonly been proposed as a basis for allocating healthcare. *We argued in favour of an egalitarian distribution according to healthcare need, with a preference for those in greatest healthcare need, those otherwise disadvantaged, and those upon whom others are dependent.* We argued against the application of standards such as provider whimsy, ability to pay, social contribution, old age, consciousness, quality of life, and personal responsibility for illness.

16.5 What mix of government and private?

In previous chapters we argued that morality does not point to any single 'right' answer to what mix of government and private health provision is required. Rather it excludes certain proposals (such as those which would abandon all but the very rich or would turn healthworkers into slaves of the state) and points to certain basic objects which must be guaranteed or at least genuinely pursued by whatever system is chosen (in particular, universal access to healthcare sufficient to satisfy genuine needs).

The Catholic principle of social justice known as *subsidiarity*, which we examined in chapter 15, became a focus of discussion in Europolitics and British political debate in the late 1980s. The NHS reforms developed in this period were sometimes attributed in part to this notion, envisaging as they did a shift from a central command-and-control system to a more pluralistic set of arrangements in which greater power has been devolved to local purchasers and providers. Despite reluctance on their part, health authorities are now expected to ration resources in accord with perceived local needs; healthworkers are increasingly required to balance the requirements of their individual patients with those of the wider community. In many countries governments have recently moved to charge healthworkers with greater responsibility for resource allocation and to leave more of healthcare provision to the operation of the 'free market' of individual providers and consumers. Even more radical proposals have included devolving to various groupings the power to define their own healthcare needs and determine their own levels of provision and preferred allocation criteria.

The principle of subsidiarity does not necessarily require decentralisation and privatization: it all depends upon what best helps the members of the society to help themselves. It may be possible for private individuals, groups (such as religious orders) and institutions (such as churches and charity hospitals) to contribute significantly to healthcare delivery. A major challenge in the coming years will be for government to co-operate with the private and voluntary health sector to ensure a just health and social care system, rather than treating it simply as a means of cost and responsibility cutting. But when private persons are unable to ensure access to basic care and allocation on a just basis, larger groupings including the state have a duty to intervene on behalf of those affected and for the good of the whole society. Thus subsidiarity may be said to give only a *prima facie* preference to the smaller, more local and more private unit. This nonetheless has implications for any paternalistic 'grand plan' of healthcare allocation: for *insofar as individuals, families and local communities can provide for their own healthcare effectively and allocate their resources justly, they should be allowed and encouraged to do so, rather than finding their decision-making power and activities absorbed by some larger unit.* Subsidiarity would also suggest that priority-setting in healthcare ought to accommodate some degree of discretion on the part of those delivering healthcare. Physicians sometimes rightly complain when rationing is taken completely out of their hands by managers But the question of 'who keeps the gate?' is perplexing physicians the world over.

16.6 Who should keep the gate?

Health professionals and bioethicists commonly resist the suggestion that healthworkers should make resource allocation decisions; they argue that this should be left to higher authorities more distant from the bedside. Thus the House of Lords Select Committee on Medical Ethics (1994) declared:

> Healthcare teams should not be put in a position of having to make such [resource allocation] decisions in the course of their day-to-day clinical practice. Their concern must be for the welfare of the individual patient. Decisions about the treatments which society can afford should be made elsewhere than in the hospital ward or the doctor's consulting room, and they should be made on the basis that such treatments as society does wish to fund must be available equally to all who can benefit from them. In particular we would emphasize that treatment-limiting decisions... should depend on the condition of the individual patient and on the appropriateness to that patient of whatever treatment or methods of management are generally available, and should not be determined by considerations of resource availability.[24]

Several reasons may be given for this position. First, that health professionals lack information about the larger picture of competing needs and rival claims, as well as the skills, experience or power to make such decisions.

Secondly, it is argued that these are ultimately ethical, financial and political decisions rather than medical ones and thus inappropriate for healthworkers. But most medical decisions have financial and political implications, and all have a moral dimension. For reasons we have already explored, it is in fact irresponsible for health professionals to make decisions on purely 'technical' grounds without regard to their moral or other implications.

Thirdly, it is argued that by leaving allocation decisions to those 'at the coalface' those at higher levels of the health system and in government are evading their responsibilities. Certainly a good case can be made for all those involved in healthcare, from the most junior healthworker to the most senior government official, accepting greater responsibility in this area; if some are evading their responsibilities, they too should be required to take their part. But to assert that leaving it to doctors and nurses is an evasion of responsibility on the part of others is to beg the question of where the prime responsibility should lie.

Fourthly, it is suggested that forcing healthworkers to act as 'gate-keepers' may adversely affect professional and organisational morale. Greater sensitivity to the effects on morale of institutional change and of additional responsibilities is certainly required and 'ideal' patterns of distribution may have to be compromised to meet such concerns. But change and new responsibilities need not result in lowered morale, especially if there is a reasonable process of consultation and co-responsibility.

Fifthly, it is said that giving health professionals a gate-keeping rôle could encourage a breach of trust and dishonest communication between healthworkers and patients. Health professionals, unhappily forced by resource shortages to limit access to a treatment, may pretend that it is 'not clinically indicated' when this is not strictly true, and patients are left unsure about the professionals' candour. But dissimulation need not be the response to shame on the part of workers, nor need they feel ashamed if gate-keeping is properly part of their rôle and this is well-publicized and understood by all concerned.

Finally, it is contended that gate-keeping is not a part of healthcare professional practice as traditionally conceived, and may be contrary to that practice: at the very least this means that health professionals will be ill-prepared to meet practical challenges in this area, and may suffer considerable unease, confusion, even practical paralysis as a result. More fundamentally, gate-keeping could be regarded as contrary to the Hippocratic ethical tradition with its commitment to the good of the *individual* patient, in so far as it makes healthworkers into double agents, with competing allegiances to different patients and rival concerns for their patients' medical needs and wider social interests. Divided allegiance is apt to give rise to breach of trust – both with the patient, who presumes the doctor will do 'everything possible' for him or her, and with the community, for whom the commitment of the doctor has that character.

This last objection is, in our view, the most powerful. Nonetheless, healthworkers have always had to decide how to ration their limited time and energies, and their patients have always been rivals for their attention at least to some extent. The NHS has long relied upon GPs, with whom patients must register, to act as informal gate-keepers, restricting 'unnecessary' and 'uneconomic' use of specialists, hospitals and other expensive resources. At least implicitly, therefore, doctors, patients and the community have long consented to rationing on some just basis where this was necessary, without thereby compromising patient trust or the healthworker's principal focus on the needs of the patient. More public and formalized articulations of this implicit understanding are probably now desirable. But the traditional focus on 'the patient in front of me' does not justify indifference to the needs of others not quite so proximate. *Professions and professionals are properly answerable not only to their clients but for the common good.*

Thus the Hippocratic duty of 'putting the patient first' needs to be carefully nuanced. In a world where it is no longer possible to do 'everything possible' for a patient – principally because so much more is now possible – we must re-emphasise that the Hippocratic duty refers only to what is truly 'possible' both *practically* (in terms not just of available technology but also of available resources) and *morally* (in terms of competing claims and duties). The just distribution of health resources requires that no-one – patients, healthworkers, health-planners, insurers or government – remain fixated myopically on the needs of one particular person *or* on maximizing aggregate health or QALY gains *or* on efficiency measures and cost containment strategies: for all are bound by the Golden Rule of Healthcare we elaborated above.

None the less *we believe a strong case can be made for shifting much of the responsibility for allocative decisionmaking away from healthworkers, while continuing to take proper cognizance of their views.* There is a difficult balance to be struck here. On the one hand, we should recognise that the commitment of healthworkers to using all their professional skills and energies to meet the healthcare needs of their particular patients has undoubtedly been very productive of good medicine and of medical advancement over the years. On the other hand, it is necessary for doctors to make at least some allocation decisions. General practitioners, for example, must determine which patients to refer to specialist consultants. The creation of primary care trusts may enable GPs to determine patterns of resource allocation which are more sensitive to the needs of the communities they serve. The clinical specialists to whom patients are referred have, in their turn, to make choices about which patients to treat and what treatments to give, inevitably with an eye on the resources available to them. There are, however, serious dangers in overloading doctors with extensive responsibility for allocation decisions. It would be more sensible to assign major decision-making on the allocation of resources to specialists in planning and administration with significant experience in healthcare practice and with particular skills in accounting and policy-making.

The community as a whole, its leaders and executive, should take responsibility for the 'big' decisions in healthcare allocation, for such decisions will radically affect the ideals and practices of the community as a whole. Healthworkers, especially physicians, are far from disinterested in what decisions are arrived at; nor should they be presumed to be representative or especially wise. As this Report makes clear, healthcare distribution is never a purely medical task, but unavoidably a philosophical, political and economic one as well. As such it requires contributions from persons with a broader range of interests and experience than healthworkers alone.

That said, we note in passing an opposing concern. In increasing efforts to gain more for the health pound and thus to appoint experts to ensure that this occurs, there is a real risk that the process of allocation may be so bureaucratized that too many resources will be diverted from an already heavily taxed system and that too many (clinical) decisions will be removed from the clinical setting. *Health professionals and managers must remain closely associated and view their work as a co-operative venture if we are to avoid failures of communication, rivalry for authority, and a 'top-heavy' system in which patients are ultimately the losers.*

16.7 The need for public debate on these matters

Healthcare allocation has, for the reasons examined in chapter 5, traditionally been largely covert and mysterious. We have noticed, for instance, the common (if erratically applied) practice in Britain of excluding people over a certain age from certain therapies without any public policy ever being adopted on this matter at a ministerial or NHS level. It is only recently that the practice has come to be visible to the general public through increasing media attention to it: doctors have generally told elderly patients 'nothing more can be done' rather than 'you're too old for the NHS resources'. Though well documented in the literature of medical ethics and practice, age rationing has remained hitherto one of the profession's best kept secrets. Invisibility of criteria can cloak arbitrariness and deception, and disables public criticism and debate. If, as we have argued in chapter 12 (12.4.3), age alone as a criterion is morally unacceptable, then the secrecy with which such a standard is applied compounds the problems. *We consider that there is need for (a) more research into alloca-tion practice in the UK; (b) publication of those criteria which are actually applied; and (c) encouragement of genuinely public debate, representative of the community at large, over what should be done in allocating healthcare resources. Healthcare professionals have an important responsibility to bring their knowledge of what is happening 'on the ground' to this debate.*

17

Summary and Conclusions

17.1   There is a recurrent debate in the UK both about the total resources that should be devoted to healthcare within our society, and about how the resources made available for health-care should be allocated. This Report is a contribution to that debate.

17.2   We welcome the fact that this debate is increasingly open. In the UK the debate centres around the NHS. Open debate about resource allocation in the NHS may not be particularly welcome to politicians especially if it serves to make transparent exactly what is attributable to their decisions. But fundamental values are at stake in the debate, so it is desirable that it should be open and that as many people as possible should interest themselves in it. Approaches to resource allocation are being advocated which will profoundly affect the character of the community in which we all live.

17.3   This Report has sought to make a quite specific and limited kind of contribution to the debate. That contribution will not be understood if readers think we aspire to provide a blueprint for resource allocation. Rather, as is appropriate for authors whose work has been sponsored by the Catholic Bishops of Great Britain and Ireland, we confine ourselves to making a critical and constructive contribution to defining the ethical framework which policy advisers and decision-makers should bear in mind in thinking about how to allocate scarce healthcare resources. An ethical framework, though it should be a decisive determinant of resource allocation policy (at least by way of excluding some options and some approaches to policy-making), is only one determinant.

17.4　On the critical side, we have found influential approaches to resource allocation in healthcare to be defective in ways that are potentially damaging to the practice of healthcare, to groups of patients, and more broadly to the character of relationships in our society. We have tried to make clear precisely what is defective in those approaches. On the constructive side, we have aimed to remedy those defects by identifying and describing the full range of considerations which need to be borne in mind if resource allocation policy is not to lead to grave injustices to certain groups of patients and seriously to damage healthcare practice.

17.5　Our critiques of various approaches may be summarised as follows:

1. A free market approach results in distributional arrangements which fall far short of what people may reasonably expect as a just allocation of healthcare. Advocates of a free market have an inadequate understanding of what is needed for human flourishing and what is therefore required for the common good.

2. Any approach to healthcare allocation based on principles which aim to be neutral between different and conflicting understandings of what is required for human flourishing has to be inadequate. Without specific, substantive understandings of the nature of persons and what is required for their well-being, questions about what kind of healthcare to allocate, to whom and on what basis cannot be given rationally defensible answers.

3. Consensus principles are not going to provide rationally defensible answers to these questions either, if consensus is determined by population surveys, and policy makers rely on majority opinion. Majority opinion is apt to reflect prejudices injurious to vulnerable groups.

4. The 'four principles' characteristic of a certain approach to bioethical issues provide no sound basis for answering these questions, since a certain vagueness in the underpinning of the principles results in a certain arbitrariness in their application.

5. Contemporary liberal-welfarist approaches to healthcare allocation, which emphasise principles of liberty, equality and fraternity, are fatally disabled by their commitment to neutrality

about the human good, i.e. about the constitutive elements of human flourishing. In consequence, a principle of liberty (or autonomy) lacks adequate criteria for distinguishing between exercises of autonomy which are consistent with the individual and common good and those which are not; a principle of equality of opportunity cannot say what human beings truly need opportunities for; and a principle of fraternity, which seeks to provide for those in 'greatest need', is unable convincingly to identify the relevant needs and ensure that proper account is taken of the claims of each kind of need.

6. There are basic objections to adopting the utilitarian type of framework for healthcare allocation which is found to be attractive by many economists. That framework characteristically evaluates healthcare interventions in terms of their 'quality-of-life' benefits. However, it is both the case that healthcare properly serves more than what utilitarianism counts as a quality-of-life benefit, and that there is no rational method of measuring or ranking those benefits. Efficiency and effectiveness are certainly important, but they are instrumental, and therefore subordinate, values: they concern means not ends. Wherever in the Report we emphasise the importance of efficiency and effectiveness we do so in relation to the achievement of what we argue to be sound objectives of policy. Efficiency and effectiveness have no free-standing claims upon us. Unfortunately, utilitarianism does not provide us with an adequate account of the proper ends of healthcare and so cannot provide the framework for the public policy we need. As we have already noted under 3 above, aggregation of community preferences cannot provide us with a rationally compelling answer to questions about the ends to be served by healthcare allocation.

17.6   Our constructive contribution to the contemporary debate begins from the observation that what is commonly lacking in all the approaches we have found to be defective is an adequate understanding of the human good; an adequate understanding of human persons; an adequate understanding of human community and the common good; and an adequate understanding of healthcare itself.

17.7   The human good – human flourishing – is constituted by our sharing in certain basic goods, goods which we all need to honour and respect, both for our own sakes and for the sake of others. Among the basic goods are life itself and health. We need to be responsive to certain positive norms if we are to share in these goods as we need to. We also need to be responsive to certain negative moral norms which are designed to protect ourselves and others from choices intended to damage or impede our sharing in basic human goods. We acquire this responsiveness in acquiring the virtues necessary for living well, moral virtues being precisely dispositions readily to choose and act in ways which foster one's own and others' flourishing. There are virtues all of us need in order to continue to enjoy the good of health. There are also virtues which doctors and nurses need if they are to be good healthcare practitioners. This last point is particularly important in considering allocation policy, for it means that a highly relevant question to ask of any such policy is: Is it consistent with doctors and nurses continuing to cultivate the virtues they need if they are to be good healthcare practitioners, or does it tend to subvert the practice of such virtues?

17.8   An adequate understanding of the human person must include the recognition that every individual human being between conception and death is a human person; all in principle have claims on the provision of healthcare. A human person is essentially a bodily being; our bodies are not extrinsic to some supposed real self. So the good of life and the good of health that are intrinsic to our well-being are the goods of bodily life and health: these are not merely instrumental means to the flourishing proper to persons. What we need in order to ensure continued sharing in basic goods should be recognised as basic needs. Given our vulnerabilities to illness and accident, healthcare is a basic need. But not everything that passes for 'healthcare' is something needed to enjoy bodily life and health. Indeed there are practices which can have no legitimacy whatever as serving a basic need, and indeed some (such as abortion) are plainly contrary to the goods of life and health. Allocation policy should be influenced by these truths. Where there is a basic need there is reason, other things being equal, to identify a corresponding duty to meet that need. Individuals capable in their circumstances of meeting their own needs have duties to do so. But many individuals, for various reasons, lack the ability adequately to meet their healthcare needs. Hence the importance of considering the role of human communities in meeting healthcare needs.

17.9   We reject those atomistic views of human association for which the idea of community means an aggregation of individuals who have little more in common than the fact that each is intent on the pursuit of his or her own ends, and who must, therefore, settle for arrangements designed to minimise conflict and maximise the opportunities of each. All of us are profoundly dependent on relationships of cooperation for our existence and for the possibilities of flourishing as human beings. Since cooperative relationships are a moral necessity they give rise to duties to sustain and create the conditions of flourishing which should exist at different levels of community. At the most fundamental level of community, the family, duties of healthcare arise precisely because of the character of the marital commitment to faithful love between spouses and for children which founds the individual family. The limited resources of families mean, however, that sophisticated and expensive healthcare requires higher levels of social organization. Hence the provision of healthcare is an important part of the common good of societies, i.e. one of those conditions of human flourishing which complex levels of social cooperation exist to serve. Because every human being has a claim to flourish, the social resources of healthcare should be distributed justly, which in the first place means *fairly* in relation to need. The requirements of justice in distributing resources may be expressed in terms of rights and duties. Societies do not have to arrive at uniform solutions to the problem of providing healthcare in order adequately to recognise the right to it. One kind of solution rather than another will to some considerable extent be dictated by a society's distinctive tradition and culture. Hence there would have to be very powerful reasons for departing from the now long-standing tradition of NHS provision of healthcare in the UK.

17.10 Finally, in seeking to remedy the intellectual defects of the approaches we criticised, we turned to a brief consideration of what is properly inherent to the practice of healthcare. The health professions have developed a particular ethic and mores precisely so that practitioners may better serve the goals or objectives of the professions. The dominant goal is health understood as the well-ordered organic functioning of the body as a whole, such as more or less well serves a human being's survival and ability to flourish in the sense we have defined, i.e. the ability to share in at least some of the other basic human goods. So the science and art of medicine are meant to secure the maintenance or restoration of health, or to secure some approximation to organic well-functioning, or to secure palliation of symptoms. The palliation of symptoms (when cure is not achievable) aims precisely to control those impediments to our sharing in other human goods which arise from organic malfunctioning. The science and art of nursing partly overlap with medicine but are distinctive in their emphasis on the care to be given to patients including basic nursing care. Healthcare practice should be informed by respect for moral values, observance of moral norms, and the practice of relevant virtues. Doctors and nurses should be disposed never intentionally to kill their patients, do violence to them or manipulate or exploit them, or neglect or abandon or lie to them. Positively, they should be disposed to respect their patients, be responsive to their real needs, reverence the lives entrusted to them, and strive to save and care for those lives, and cure where possible. Doctors and nurses, therefore, need to be people with a strong sense of justice, of charity, and of solidarity with those whom they serve. But it is not only the patients who will suffer if those dispositions are lacking; so will the doctors and nurses who cannot truly flourish in their professional vocations without them. Allocational arrangements should not place undue strain on the cultivation and maintenance of those dispositions. If the care of certain types of patient is under-resourced and those patients are already frail, dependent and vulnerable, then the temptation to neglect, abandon or even kill those patients can become pressing.

17.11 In the light of what we have to say about the human good, human persons, human community and healthcare practice, we reject as inadequate or simply misguided a number of criteria for healthcare allocation. In particular, we reject the view that access to healthcare should depend on a patient's social contribution, or age, or possession of a minimum quality of life or level of mental ability, or on a record of responsible behaviour in regard to health. These are all dangerously discriminatory criteria for access to healthcare. The principal determinant of orders of priority among patients, among patient groups, and among treatments, should be healthcare need. We offer detailed indications for discriminating between more and less important, and more and less pressing healthcare need. Healthcare need should be addressed in order of importance, and preference given to patients and patient groups in greater need. The requirement that there should be equality of access applies only after one has determined which patients are most in need of healthcare. Considerations of effectiveness and efficiency should influence what is done to meet healthcare need but should not determine priority of need. For there are groups of patients who can benefit little therapeutically but who nonetheless have needs for healthcare which it is important to meet, since healthcare is for such patients the most appropriate expression of our respect for them and solidarity with them – values which should inform the whole healthcare system.

17.12 In a society like the UK, the total resources available for healthcare should be sufficient to ensure access for all to a level of healthcare adequate to satisfy genuine needs within a reasonable time and without unreasonable disincentives. This will include the provision of basic public health measures, primary care, emergency services, and hospital-based services of proven value. The ideals of the NHS – universality and comprehensiveness of access, irrespective of factors other than medical need – are admirable in principle, but there is less and less of a political sense that they are achievable ideals. Spending levels, or allocation systems or policies which fall short of meeting genuine healthcare needs require convincing ethical justification. Such justification will not be available if reasonable steps have not been taken to eliminate inefficiencies and waste, such as unnecessary administrative costs, excessive profit margins (of suppliers), ethically and medically inappropriate treatments, and tests and treatments of only marginal benefit. Nor will such justification be available if, where it is politically possible, taxation is not set at levels adequate to make truly necessary social provision for basic needs.

17.13 We would strongly emphasise that the requirements of distributive justice are not the only requirements which need to be borne in mind in healthcare allocation. Respect for other values and for basic human rights must also be borne in mind. It is clear that in our society we act contrary to respect for the rights to life and bodily integrity precisely in the allocation of healthcare resources in funding abortion, embryo experimentation, sterilization, and other forms of medically unnecessary mutilation. Furthermore, an increasing body of evidence has emerged in recent years of such frequent neglect of the frail elderly and severely mentally impaired that it appears to be systemic. The most extreme expression of this tendency is the policy of withdrawing tubefeeding from those who have suffered severe mental impairment but are *not* dying and who are thereby caused to die of starvation. In the case of patients who are irreversibly unconscious, this policy has been approved by the Courts in *Bland* and the series of cases which followed. It is vital to the restoration of a just policy of care for the frail elderly and all those judged to have a 'poor quality of life' that that part of the *Bland* judgment should be reversed which permits omission of treatment or care intended to end a patient's life.

17.14 A strong case can be made for clear legislative recognition of a right to healthcare, suitably delimited to genuine healthcare need, which could ground proceedings before some tribunal when it is the case that a person has been unjustly denied appropriate treatment.

17.15 Because of the evidence, noted at various points in this Report, of unjust discrimination against the elderly, and particularly the cognitively impaired elderly, there is a strong case for specific legislation to outlaw such discrimination in the allocation of healthcare resources.

17.16 Basic human rights, and the need to maintain solidarity with the vulnerable, require that in our society sufficient resources should be devoted to provide good care for the elderly, the mentally ill, the cognitively impaired, the newborn and the poor.

17.17 We believe that in the UK our history and culture support universal cradle-to-grave healthcover by the state, pegged at a level which will not force substantial numbers to seek alternative provision.

17.18 Clinicians should have to make only those resource allocation decisions which are unavoidable in virtue of the limits of resources available to them, i.e. decisions about which patients they can treat and what treatment to give to individual patients. The energies and commitment of doctors and nurses should, in so far as possible, be clearly patient-centred. Those with administrative responsibilities should be directly responsible for the allocation of resources for particular kinds of treatment, for particular classes of patient, and for particular forms of organizational provision. Administrators, however, need to pay close attention to the advice of clinicians if their decisions are to be appropriate to patient need.

17.19 We consider that there is need for (a) more research into allocation practice in the UK; (b) publication of those criteria which are actually applied; and (c) encouragement of genuinely public debate, representative of the community at large, over what should be done in allocating healthcare resources. Healthcare professionals have an important responsibility to bring their knowledge of what is happening 'on the ground' to this debate.

17.20 We would emphasise again that we have not undertaken to specify a policy for healthcare allocation, merely a framework of ethical considerations which ought to help shape such a policy. Certainly we have argued for excluding from provision procedures and 'treatments' which are morally objectionable or do not meet genuine healthcare needs, and we have argued for adequate provision for patient groups that are in danger not merely of neglect but also of abuse. But the aggregate of those inclusions and exclusions does not amount to an overall resource allocation policy. Many considerations other than ethical ones must enter into the formulation of such a policy. The ethical ones are fundamental, however, if policy is to avoid serious injustice to patients, the abandonment of values essential to healthcare practice, and the subversion of the moral character of medicine and nursing.

Endnotes

Chapter 1

1. World Health Organization. Constitution adopted by the Inter-
    national Health Conference, New York. *Official Record of the
    World Health Organization* 2, no. 100. 1946; see D. Callahan,
    'The WHO definition of health'. 1/3 (1973) *Hastings Center
    Report*: 77–88. The WHO has recognised that its expansive
    definition of health makes the setting of health policy targets
    impossible. So it now offers as a 'working definition' of the
    overall objective for target-setting for healthcare: 'The reduction
    in mortality, morbidity and disability due to detectable diseases
    or disorder, and an increase in the perceived level of health'.
    WHO Regional Office for Europe, *Health 21: Health for All in
    the 21st Century*. Copenhagen: WHO 1999: 211.

2. This is not to deny that sick or handicapped people can often
    come to terms with and even 'transcend' their psychophysical
    limitations.

3. As Kilner argues: 'Even in its fuller sense, happiness is a false
    goal for medicine. By gerrymandering the definition of health
    to comprise 'a state of complete physical, mental, and social
    well-being', the World Health Organization has in effect main-
    tained that happiness is the doctor's business (even if he needs
    outside partners in this enterprise). Complete mental well-
    being – not to speak of the more elusive and ambiguous
    'social well-being' ... – goes well beyond the medical province
    of sanity, depending as it does on the successful and satisfying
    exercise of intelligence, awareness, imagination, taste, prudence,

good sense, and fellow-feeling, for whose cultivation medicine can do little.' J. F. Kilner, *Who Lives? Who Dies? Ethical Criteria in Patient Selection*. New Haven & London: Yale University Press 1990: 160.

Chapter 2

1. On the history of the NHS see Geoffrey Rivett, *From Cradle to Grave. Fifty Years of the NHS*. London: King's Fund 1997.

2. Ministry of Health (UK), *A National Health Service*. London: HMSO 1944; Ministry of Health (UK), *The National Health Service Bill: A Summary of the Proposed Service*. London: HMSO 1946.

3. Office of Health Economics, *Compendium of Health Statistics* 1997, Table 2.2 gives a figure of 6.9% for 1994.

4. Health spending per head by age, 1993–94

Age	*Total £s*
Births	1,980
0–4	531
5–15	314
16–44	388
45–64	503
65–74	952
75–84	1,633
85+	2,613

   Source: Anthony Harrison, Jennifer Dixon, Bill New and Ken Judge, 'Can the NHS Cope in Future?', *British Medical Journal*, vol. 314, 1997, pp. 139–42.

5. Already a decade ago the practice of 'defensive medicine', such as duplicate tests and extensive documentation as a shield against malpractice claims, was estimated to add $15 billion to US healthcare costs *per annum* (K. Sawyer, 'High-tech cures and aging patients push U.S. health spending off the chart'. *International Herald Tribune* 31 December 1991: 3). The resistance of UK courts to such enormous damages has meant that they

have not become such a major element in healthcare costs in the UK, but they could become so in the future.

6. See Office of Health Economics, *Compendium of Health Statistics*, 1997, gives as the average per capita spending in OECD countries in 1994 a figure of £1,101 compared with UK expenditure of £787.

7. See chapter 12.4.3.

8. See Secretary of State for Health, *The New NHS. Modern – Dependable*, 5. Primary Care Groups. London: The Stationery Office: 32–43. For the legislation see *Health Act 1999. Chapter 8*. London: The Stationery Office 1999. In phase one of their anticipated development primary care groups are advisory panels to the health authority, but when fully-fledged they become primary care NHS trusts with full responsibility for commissioning health care (and accountable for results) according to service agreements made with the health authority and with secondary and specialist care trusts.

Chapter 3

1. Government Committee on Choices in Health Care, *Choices in Health Care*. Zoetermeer, The Netherlands 1992: 43.

2. With the establishment of the 'Resource Allocation Working Party' (RAWP) in 1977 secondary care budgets were formally allocated to regional health authorities on the basis of a formula providing a rough estimate of relative need; these regional allocations were in turn distributed to district health authorities, though with no clear formula; and these funds were allocated to units within the district in a 'piecemeal and individual', 'collegial' or 'quasi-feudal' way (A. Weale, ed. *Cost and Choice in Health Care: The Ethical Dimension*. King Edward Hospital Fund for London 1988: 33–34). Increasingly in recent years social deprivation was taken into account.

3. R. Klein, 'Rationality and rationing: diffused or concentrated decision-making?' in M. Tunbridge (ed.) *Rationing of Health*

Care in Medicine. London: Royal College of Physicians 1993: 73, referring to R. Klein & S. Redmayne, *Patterns of Priorities*. Birmingham: National Association of Health Authorities and Trusts 1992.

Chapter 4

1. See J. M. Finnis, *Natural Law and Natural Rights*. Oxford: Clarendon Press 1980: ch. 7; G. G. Grisez, *The Way of the Lord Jesus*, Vol. 2: *Living a Christian Life*. Quincy, Illinois: Franciscan Press 1993: 320ff.

2. Finnis, *Natural Law and Natural Rights*: 165.

3. This is the classical definition offered by Aristotle, Ulpian and Aquinas.

4. A. MacIntyre, *Whose Justice? Which Rationality?* London: Duckworth 1988: ch. 1.

Chapter 5

1. Kilner, *Who Lives? Who Dies? Ethical Criteria in Patient Selection*: 17.

2. R. Nozick, *Anarchy, State and Utopia*. Oxford: Blackwell 1974: 178–180.

3. Nozick, however, argues that a medical researcher who synthesizes a new substance that effectively treats a certain disease and who refuses to sell except on his terms does not worsen the situation of others by depriving them of whatever he or she has made: Locke's famous proviso (that one must leave 'enough and as good' for others when appropriating from nature) focuses on the way that appropriative actions affect others, rather than the structure of the situation that results (Nozick, *Anarchy, State and Utopia*: 181). Since our researcher only appropriated easily available chemicals which anyone could as easily appropriate, he or she has not breached the

'proviso'. But if healthcare is largely a social product, as we will argue, Nozick's account is unsatisfactory.

4. Nozick, *Anarchy, State and Utopia*: 169–172.

5. It is on the basis of this alternative view that common morality, including Catholic social teaching, has insisted that private property-holders still have certain redistributive duties. Thus Finnis (*Natural Law and Natural Rights*: 173) describes the natural law view that in justice the owners of private property and dependents are entitled to first use and enjoyment of it and its fruits (rents, profits, ...) as this enhances autonomy, security, productivity and care. But beyond such reasonable use and enjoyment, the remainder of the property and its fruits is held by the 'owner' as part of 'the common stock'. Thus what was commonly available but was made private (for the common good), becomes again, in justice, part of the common stock. He further notes that 'from this point, the owner has, in justice, duties not altogether unlike those of a trustee in English law. He may fulfil them in various ways – by investing his surplus in production of more goods for later distribution and consumption; by providing gainful employment to people looking for work; by grants or loans to hospitals, schools, cultural centres, orphanages, etc., or directly for the relief of the poor. Where owners will not perform these duties, or cannot effectively coordinate their respective efforts to perform them, then public authority may rightly help them to perform them by devising and implementing schemes of distribution, e.g. by 'redistributive' taxation for purposes of 'social welfare', or by a measure of expropriation.' cf. J. M. Boyle, 'The developing consensus on the right to health care', in M. Kelly (ed.) *Justice and Health Care*. St. Louis, MO: Catholic Health Association of the United States 1985: 75–90, at 81.

6. That one leaves 'enough and as good for others'; that what one takes is not 'left to spoil'; that the rich assist the poor out of their 'surplus'; and that where those with more than they need fail to assist those whose very preservation is at risk, the latter may take what they need: John Locke, *First Treatise on Civil Government* 1690: paras 41–42; *Second Treatise on Civil Government* 1690: paras. 26, 31–34, 46. Nozick, *Anarchy, State and Utopia* (at 175) recognises that if persons can initially acquire something only

if doing so does not worsen the position of others, then a strong case could be made that much of the property that is presently owned privately is held unjustly.

7.   B. A. O. Williams, 'The minimal state', in J. Paul (ed.) *Reading Nozick: Essays on 'Anarchy, State and Utopia'*. Oxford: Blackwell 1982: 27–36, at 35.

8.   Nozick, *Anarchy, State and Utopia*: 153, 231.

9.   The 'Prior Consent Model' of Menzel (see P. Menzel, *Strong Medicine: The Ethical Rationing of Healthcare*. Oxford: Oxford University Press 1990) and the hypothetical insurance account of Dworkin (see R. Dworkin, 'What is equality? Part 1: Equality of welfare', 10 [1981] *Philosophy and Public Affairs*: 185–246, and 'What is equality? Part 2: Equality of resources', 10 [1981] *Philosophy and Public Affairs*: 283–345) and Rakowski (J. Rakowski, *Equal Justice*. Oxford: Oxford University Press 1991) are all based on the notion of some actual or imputed universal consent. Here free-market theory merges with contractarian welfarism (considered in chapter 7).

Chapter 6

1.   See Dworkin, 'What is equality? Part 1: Equality of welfare' and 'What is equality? Part 2: Equality of resources'; J. Rawls, *A Theory of Justice*. London: Oxford University Press 1972; and J. Rawls, *Political Liberalism*. New York: Columbia University Press 1993.

2.   E. J. Emanuel, *The Ends of Human Life: Medical Ethics in a Liberal Polity*. Cambridge, Mass.: Harvard University Press 1991; R. Rodewaid, 'Does liberalism rest on a mistake?' 15 (1985) *Canadian Journal of Philosophy*: 231–252.

3.   This approach is most famously outlined by Rawls in *A Theory of Justice,* but similiar approaches have been taken by many 'liberal' and 'social contract' theorists.

4.   Finnis, *Natural Law and Natural Rights*: 109; M. Walzer, *Spheres of Justice*. Oxford: Robertson 1983: 79.

5. This approach is itself sometimes to be found in Rawls, but more clearly in 'communitarian'writers such as Walzer.

6. Thus a telephone poll of Oregon citizens designed to estimate how most people would evaluate various physical disabilities as reducing the value of normal health found that substance abuse and unwanted fertility were rated as very grave impairments, whereas terminal illness in the elderly and those with AIDS was given a low ranking, with the implication that terminal care was neither essential nor particularly important.

7. People who live 'objectively' restricted lives commonly accommodate in various ways, modify their values and expectations, and assess their own quality of life as much higher than others expect. Several studies have shown, for instance, that more old people want invasive care of various types, including cardiopulmonary resuscitation, than is assumed even by their own doctors, nurses and relatives; see, e.g. J. Grimley-Evans, 'Health care rationing and elderly people', in M. Tunbridge (ed.) *Rationing of Health Care in Medicine*. London: Royal College of Physicians 1993: 43–54, at 49; A. B. Seckler *et al.*, 'Substituted judgement: how accurate are proxy predictions?' 115 (1991) *Annals of Internal Medicine*: 92–98. Cancer patients, too, are much more willing to accept chemotherapy than others who do not have cancer and make their judgment from a 'safe distance': see M. L. Slevin *et al.*, 'Attitudes to chemotherapy: comparing views of patients with cancer with those of doctors, nurses and the general public'. 300 (1990) *British Medical Journal*: 1458–1460. D. L. Sackett and G. W. Torrance ['The utility of different health states as perceived by the general public'. 31 (1978) *Journal of Chronic Disease*: 697–704)] found that the value placed by individuals on treatment for chronic disease was much affected by whether they have or have had the disease themselves.

8. Weale usefully distinguishes two conceptions of the rôle of government: responsive and responsible. *Responsive* government is want-regarding, and seeks to satisfy the desires of its citizens, whatever they might be; *responsible* government is reason-respecting, seeking to adopt the right course of action even if this is unpopular at the time. He argues that any attempt on the part of government to be want-regarding (by, for instance,

polling the community on the appropriate level of, and rationing principles for, healthcare) will (a) depend upon the particular voting rule adopted by the government and (b) inevitably mean that many people's wants will remain unsatisfied because they will diverge substantially from the average level approved by the community. A reason-respecting government, on the other hand, will seek publicly and honestly to justify a course of action rather than act as a device for the satisfaction of amalgamated diverse preferences. Unavoidably such an attempt at public justification will involve appeal to the political culture of the society in question and the (often complex and contentious) values embedded therein. He argues that it should be possible to state, even if only in broad terms, what standard and quality of healthcare is expected to be yielded from a particular allocative process or decision and for whom. (This would include statistical standards concerning waiting times and other costs to the patient, recovery rates and other quality of care indicators.) The government would then be expected to revise its allocation or its service expectation if it could be shown that the putative standard of provision can not be met with the existing resources policy. (A. Weale, 'The allocation of scarce medical resources: a democrat's dilemma', in P. Byrne (ed.) *Ethics and Law in Health Care and Research*. Chichester: Wiley 1990: 116–130.)

9. Examples include: T. L. Beauchamp and J. Childress, *Principles of Biomedical Ethics* [fourth edition] London: Oxford University Press 1994; R. Gillon, *Philosophical Medical Ethics*. Chichester: Wiley 1986; R. Gillon (ed.), *Principles of Health Care Ethics*. Chichester: Wiley 1994.

10. See earlier editions of Beauchamp and Childress.

11. See, for example, the following from the third edition of the Beauchamp and Childress textbook: 'articles on research that uses double-blind techniques and deceives patients sometimes denounce the research as unjustly denying subjects information to which they have a right. Here the controlling moral principle is not of justice but rather of respect for autonomy . . . Similarly, proponents of a physician's obligation to withhold potentially harmful information from patients for therapeutic reasons sometimes argue that it would be unjust for the physician to disclose

the information. Here the moral concern is either nonmaleficence or beneficence rather than justice ... our argument about
prima facie principles supports the conclusion that principles
of justice do not always triumph over other principles.' (p. 257)
In similar vein: R. M. Veatch, *A Theory of Medical Ethics*. New
York: Basic Books 1981.

12. A. Weale (ed.) *Cost and Choice in Health: The Ethical Dimension*.
London: King Edward's Hospital Fund for London 1988, for
instance, is fairly representative in equating all failures to treat
for whatever reason with acts of killing or abandonment (see
p. 21).

Chapter 7

1. Rawls, for instance, does not include healthcare among his
schedule of 'all-purpose social primary goods' which are the
subject-matter of distributive justice; on the face of it, then,
his theory has nothing to say to the question of healthcare
allocation. Several writers have sought by creative exegesis to
find healthcare hidden among Rawls' list of primary goods, or
else to reconstruct the theory so that opportunities for healthcare
are provided and some directions found as to how best to ration
(see note 2 below). But this only serves to emphasize the limitations of so 'thin' a theory of the good.

2. While Rawls himself tends to use the term 'opportunity' to refer
only to access to jobs and goods useful in the competition for the
better jobs, some of his followers have proposed expanding the
category to include healthcare (e.g. N. Daniels, *Just Health Care*.
Cambridge: Cambridge University Press 1985; T. W. M. Pogge,
Realizing Rawls. Ithaca, NY: Cornell University Press 1989) – a
move which Rawls himself has recently approved, suggesting
that the aim of healthcare is 'to restore people so that once
again they are fully cooperating members of society' (Rawls,
Political Liberalism: 184–186).

3. Daniels recognizes that the opportunity approach can lead to
'the troubling conclusion' that terminal care and care for the
seriously mentally and physically disabled, which provide little

hope of attaining this goal, are not required by justice (*Just Health Care*: 48).

4. This is an important negative stipulation, as it is clear that allocation on these sorts of grounds is not uncommon. It is in keeping both with the common assertion that access to health-care is an entitlement for all, and with a traditional medical ethic. However, some 'liberals' would allow 'discrimination' against the permanently unconscious or otherwise severely mentally handicapped, the elderly, and those who brought their conditions upon themselves. See chapter 12.

5. Thus, for instance, preferential treatment might be given among others to great benefactors of the poor or to great doctors who treat the poor, or as an incentive or compensation for those who engage in socially beneficial (and possibly) risky works.

6. T. Nagel, *Equality and Partiality*. New York: Oxford University Press 1991: 67–73.

Chapter 8

1. The literature on QALYs and other methods used in health eco-nomics is now vast. For a recent clear introduction see chapter 3 of E. Nord, *Cost Value Analysis in Health Care: Making Sense of QALYs*. Cambridge: Cambridge University Press 1999.

2. On the Oregon Plan see, for a brief overview, M. Brannigan, 'Oregon's Experiment'. In D. Seedhouse (ed.) *Reforming Health Care. The Philosophy and Practice of International Health Reform*. Chichester: Wiley 1995: 27–52.

3. A. Maynard, 'The economics of rationing health care'. In M. Tunbridge (ed.) *Rationing of Health Care in Medicine*. London: Royal College of Physicians 1993: 1–12, at 6.

4. On the Oregon Plan, in addition to M. Brannigan, 'Oregon's Experiment', see F. Honigsbaum, J. Calltorp, C. Ham and S. Holmstrom, *Priority Setting Processes for Healthcare*. Oxford and New York: Radcliffe Medical Press 1995: 11–21; M. A. Strosberg,

J. M. Wiener, R. Baker with I. A. Fein (eds) *Rationing America's Medical Care: The Oregon Plan and Beyond*. Washington, D.C., The Brookings Institution 1992.

5.   Costs were based on average charges in Oregon including diagnosis, hospitalization, professional services, prescribed drugs and ancillary services; outcome data were collected from a literature search supplemented by 29 speciality panels composed of doctors; quality of life was calculated by sorting patients into 23 symptom categories, assessing their mobility, physical activity and social activity, and assigning 'QALY decrement values' on the basis of a phone survey of 1,001 respondents.

6.   Health promotion, mental health and substance abuse services were excluded.

7.   Maynard, 'The Economics of rationing health care'.

8.   J. Harris, 'Unprincipled QALYs: a response to Cubbon'. 17 (1991) *Journal of Medical Ethics*: 185–188.

9.   F. Honigsbaum, *Who Shall Live? Who Shall Die? Oregon's Health Financing Proposals*. London: King's Fund 1991: 43–45.

10. D. W. Brock, 'The value of prolonging human life'. 50 (1986) *Philosophical Studies*: 401–428; A. E. Buchanan, 'Health care delivery and resource allocation'. In R. M. Veatch (ed.) *Medical Ethics*. Boston: Jones and Bartlett: 1989: 291–327, at 299–300.

11. G. Grisez, 'Against Consequentialism', 23 (1978) *American Journal of Jurisprudence*: 21–72, at 29–41.

12. See E. Anderson, *Value in Ethics and Economics*. Cambridge, Mass., and London: Harvard University Press 1993: 5; Finnis, *Natural Law and Natural Rights*: 113–115; Grisez, 'Against Consequentialism': 33.

13. J. M. Finnis, 'Economics, justice and the value of life: concluding remarks'. In L. Gormally (ed.) *The Dependent Elderly. Autonomy, Justice and Quality of Care*. Cambridge: Cambridge University Press 1992: 190; J. M. Finnis, J. Boyle and G. Grisez, *Nuclear*

Deterrence, Morality and Realism. Oxford: Oxford University Press 1987: 243–272; Grisez, 'Against Consequentialism': 41–49. These authors conclude that utilitarianism is not merely a theory with difficulties, but one that is literally meaningless.

14. For instance, Maynard, 'The Economics of rationing health care', 1: 'choices are unavoidable and should be made explicitly to foster efficiency and accountability ... Ideally, scarce health-care resources should be allocated to maximize improvements in 'health gain', and in the length and quality of life. A failure to behave efficiently (i.e. to improve health to the greatest extent at least cost) is unethical.'

15. e.g. K. Calman, 'Decision making and the National Health Service: making choices in the real world'. In M. Tunbridge (ed.) *Rationing of Health Care in Medicine.* London: Royal College of Physicians 1993: 25–32.

16. Weale (ed.), *Cost and Choice in Health Care: The Ethical Dimension* at 55 notes some of the characteristic conclusions we have in mind: 'The traditional ethic of medical treatment enjoins all those responsible for the care of the sick to do their utmost to effect a cure. The logic of economic calculation is to trade off benefits against costs. The traditional ethic requires that those who care for the sick focus their attention on the specific person in front of them. The logic of economic calculation is to consider the effects of individual decisions on all those who are touched by their consequences. The traditional ethic requires that the maintenance of individual life be given supreme value. The logic of economic calculation is to allow that individuals' lives may be sacrificed in order to achieve a benefit elsewhere.'

17. J. Harris, 'EQALYty'. In P. Byrne (ed.) *Health, Rights and Resources: King's College Studies 1987–1988.* London: King Edward's Hospital Fund for London 1988: 100–127, at 108.

18. Harris, 'EQALYty': 109.

19. See J. Boyle, G. Grisez and O. Tollefsen, *Free Choice: A Self-Referential Argument.* Notre Dame: University of Notre Dame

Press 1976; Finnis, Boyle and Grisez, *Nuclear Deterrence, Morality and Realism*: 253; J. M. Finnis and A. Fisher, 'Theology and the four principles: a Roman Catholic view'. In R. Gillon (ed.) *Principles of Health Care Ethics*. Chichester: Wiley 1993: 31–44; H. McCabe, *Law, Love and Language*. London: Sheed & Ward 1968.

20. See Finnis, 'Economics, justice and the value of life: concluding remarks' at 191: 'Whichever proposal is adopted or recommended, the choice (or recommendation) is one which will impact on the character of the chooser (or recommender) and of every potential chooser, on the character of healthcare professionals, on the relationship of trust between healthcare professionals and their clients, on the attitude of everyone to his or her own body and bodily life, on the whole substance of solidarity between the strong and the weak at all stages of life... And all these effects quite elude measurement, yet are very real and are really involved, as benefits and harms, in the only relevant object of weighing and comparing: the alternative *options* (of treating/sustaining, of killing, and of abandoning the patient) to be considered in deliberation and accepted or rejected in free choice.'

Chapter 9

1. As Grisez, Boyle and Finnis argue, insofar as these basic goods are 'reasons with no further reasons' they are primary principles, diverse categories, and so incommensurable with each other. To be truly commensurable, these basic goods would have to be either homogeneous in all relevant respects (and thus not truly diverse), or reducible to some other more basic good(s) by which they could be compared (and thus not truly primary). Thus no basic good considered precisely as such can meaningfully be said to be better or worse than any other. The basic goods are called 'good' because they are rationally desired, not because there is any single reason underlying every reasonable purpose, like the utilitarian concepts of utility, pleasure or preference fulfilment we discussed in chapter 8. Instantiations of goods in the purposes for which we choose to act can also be incommensurable even when they are instantiations of one and the same basic good because neither option may promise everything promised by its alternative. (G. Grisez, J. Boyle

and J. M. Finnis, 'Practical principles, moral truth and ultimate ends'. 32 (1987) *American Journal of Jurisprudence*: 99–151, at 110.)

2.   Kass considers the Hippocratic model of the virtuous physician: just, moderate, self-restrained, grave, generous, discrete, prudent, reverent. (L. Kass, *Toward a More Natural Science. Biology and Human Affairs*. New York: The Free Press 1985: 240.)

3.   Kass, *loc cit*.

Chapter 10

1.   We reject the kind of dualism embraced by a number of contemporary bioethicists who treat ' personhood' as a function of characteristics which a living human being acquires and may lose while remaining a living human being. The distinction between human persons and human beings is made in an inevitably arbitrary fashion and invoked to rationalise seriously unjust treatment of immature and impaired human beings. See further 12.4.4 of this Report and L. Gormally (ed.) *Euthanasia, Clinical Practice and the Law*. London: The Linacre Centre 1994: 124–6.

2.   Though, of course, even people with great disabilities or illnesses can still choose and act within those confines.

3.   V. R. Fuchs, 'Rationing healthcare'. 311 (1984) *New England Journal of Medicine*: 1572–1573. The figures he gives are probably optimistic.

4.   A. L. Cochrane, *Effectiveness and Efficiency*. London: Nuffield Provincial Hospitals Trust 1972; L. Doyal and L. Doyal, 'Western scientific medicine: a philosophical and political prognosis'. In L. Birke and J. Silvertown (eds) *More than the Parts: The Politics of Biology*. London: Pluto Press 1984; I. Illich, 'Clinical damage, medical monopoly, the expropriation of health'. 1 (1975) *Journal of Medical Ethics*: 78–80; R. Rhodes, *Health Care Politics, Policy and Distributive Justice: the Ironic Triumph*. New York: New York State University Press 1992. Smith estimates that only about 15% of medical interventions are supported by 'hard' scientific evidence of outcomes; much of medical knowledge is

of a 'softer' kind based on clinical experience and hunch. (R. Smith, 'Where is the wisdom...? The poverty of medical evidence'. 303 (1991) *British Medical Journal*: 1561–2.)

5. Carlson considered five variables that influence health and ranks them according to their importance: (1) environment, (2) lifestyle, (3) society, (4) genetics, and (5) medical care. He assessed the contribution of healthcare at approximately 6%. (R. J. Carlson, *The End of Medicine*. New York: Wiley 1975)

6. J. B. McKinlay and S. M. McKinlay, 'The questionable contribution of medical measures to the decline of mortality in the United States in the twentieth century'. 55 (1977) *Milbank Memorial Fund Quarterly*: 405–428. Kass (*Toward a More Natural Science*: 163) notes that from 1900 to 1970 the average life expectancy of white males in the US at age 65 increased by only one and a half years. He shows that 'the complete eradication of heart disease, cancer, and stroke – currently the major mortal diseases – would, according to some calculations, extend the average life expectancy... at age sixty-five by no more than one and a half to two years. In the US medicine's contribution to longer life has nearly reached its natural limit.' Most improvements in life-expectancy have in fact come through public health measures such as sewerage, improved nutrition and sanitation, socio-economic provision such as welfare and housing, and low-tech medicine such as immunizations and antibiotics. Mainstream healthcare is not as statistically significant for health as is commonly assumed.

7. See L. Gormally (ed.) *Euthanasia, Clinical Practice and the Law*. London: The Linacre Centre 1994: 62–64, 138–141.

Chapter 11

1. See St. Thomas Aquinas, *Summa theologiae* 2a 2ae q.47, art. 10 ad 2.

2. MacIntyre in *After Virtue* describes a 'tradition' as (a) a set of practices, (b) a mode of understanding the importance and worth of those practices, (c) a medium by which such practices are shaped, and (d) the means by which such practices are transmitted across generations.

3. See Finnis, *Natural Law and Natural Rights*: 136–138; Walzer, *Spheres of Justice*: 228–229; Kass: 'the household, that nest and nursery of humanity – private, intimate, and vulnerable. Though its roots are the needs of bodily life – nurture, protection, reproduction, and then protection and nurture of the young – the household provides for more than the body. A richly woven fabric of nature and convention, it is established by law to nurture our nature. It is sustained by customs that humanize the human animal, engendering love and friendship, speech and education, choice and awareness, and shared beliefs and feelings.' (*Toward a More Natural Science*: 237)

4. Finnis suggests: 'Only a family or quasi-family can build up over time that common stock – of uncalculated affection, physical and psychological rapport, of shelter and means of support and material bases for new projects, of memories and experience, of symbols, signs, and gestures to bear moods and meanings, of knowledge of each other's strengths and weaknesses, loves and detestations, and of formal and informal but reliable commitment and devotion – which each member holds at the others' disposal, and which... constitutes an incomparably fine thing for a friend to give or to receive.' (*Natural Law and Natural Rights*: 145)

5. e.g. *Bland* (1993) per Hoffmann L. J. at 356, 367: 'If someone allows a small child or invalid in his care to starve to death... we think he has committed a particularly wicked crime... It is the same ethical principle which requires doctors and hospitals to provide the patients in their care with such medical attention and nursing as they are reasonably able to give... We should, if we are able to do so, provide food and shelter to a human being in our care who is unable to provide for himself.'

6. Finnis, *Natural Law and Natural Rights*: 166–167. cf. Aristotle, *Nicomachean Ethics* 1130b31–33, 1131b27–32.

7. To argue that healthcare is properly a distributable 'resource' is not, however, to argue that health professionals should be treated like hospital beds or doses of drugs which can be moved about, reorganized, reassigned to new duties, and so forth, at the whim of health planners. Unlike inanimate resources, health-workers are themselves members of the moral community

served by the distribution: to fail to treat them with respect for their dignity as persons, but merely as means to some distributive pattern, is to fail to take part of the population into account in assessing the common good. Furthermore, as human beings their efficient and happy functioning will require a certain amount of continuity, predictability, building up of teamwork, and so forth. These points have important implications for any reform strategies.

8.   Boyle ('The developing consensus on the right to health care': 87) observes: 'it would be a gross violation of the Golden Rule to refuse to anyone a kind of socially organized assistance that each of us wants for ourselves and for those we love'. He elsewhere asks: 'Does the system provide to all that standard of healthcare people reasonably want for themselves and their loved ones and would judge themselves obliged to provide to their neighbours in need?... When we are ill or when those near and dear to us are ill, we reasonably want and need the help of others in dealing with the situation. For when we are ill we are especially dependent and vulnerable... To want such help for oneself and for those we love, but not to be ready to give it to others when we can is to play favourites – to fail to be ready to do for others what one reasonably wants them to do for oneself – and this is to violate the Golden Rule.' (J. M. Boyle, 'The right to health care and its limits'. In D. G. McCarthy (ed.) *Scarce Medical Resources and Justice*. St. Louis, MO: Pope John Center 1987: 13–25, at 15, 22–23).

9.   By a simple application of the Golden Rule Boyle identifies further priority rules in healthcare allocation: 'priority will be given to providing the basic care children need to get a decent start in life, to similar help for those who because of poverty or other deprivation cannot provide for their own healthcare, and to first contact care, diagnosis, and pain control for everybody. These are minimally the relatively simple things which decent people would want for themselves and seek for their dependents and neighbours, and which the healthcare system can surely facilitate their providing. These services should, I think, take priority in healthcare over more exotic treatments for those who can take for granted such minimally adequate healthcare.' ('The right to health care and its limits': 23.)

10. On the doctrine of the surplus and the duty to redistribute it see: Finnis, *Natural Law and Natural Rights*: 173; C. Fried, 'Distributive justice', 1 (1983) *Social Philosophy and Policy*: 45–59; G. Grisez, *Living a Christian Life*: 811; B. A. Lustig, 'Needy persons and rationed resources'. In C. S. Campbell and B. A. Lustig (eds) *Duties to Others*. Dordrecht: Kluwer 1994.

11. An adequate understanding of justice is what is required to avoid the overinflated rhetoric of rights characteristic of much contemporary debate.

12. Finnis, *Natural Law and Natural Rights*: 218–219.

13. Finnis, *Natural Law and Natural Rights*: 219–220.

14. J. M. Boyle, 'The concept of health and the right to health care'. 3 (1977) *Social Thought*: 5–17; A. MacIntyre, 'Patients as agents'. In S. F. Spicker and T. Englehardt (eds) *Philosophical Medical Ethics: Its Nature and Significance*. Dordrecht: Reidel 1977: 197–212, at 206–207.

15. Kass, *Towards a More Natural Science*: chs 8 & 9; E. Pellegrino and D. Thomasma, *For the Patient's Good: The Restoration of Beneficence in Health Care*. Oxford: Oxford University Press 1988: 66–68.

16. Declaration of Geneva 1948 (revised 1968 and 1983).

Introduction to Part IV

1. These are the five identified in the well-known treatment of the subject in G. Outka, 'Social justice and equal access to health care'. 2 (1974) *Journal of Religious Ethics*: 11–32, at 12.

Chapter 12

1. See D. Orentlicher, 'Rationing and the Americans with Disabilities Act'. 271 (1994) *Journal of the American Medical Association*: 308–314. The 1946 NHS Bill stated that the NHS

'imposes no limits on availability e.g. limitations based on financial means, age, sex, employment or vocation, area of residence
or insurance qualification': [281]. United Nations, *International
Covenant of Economic, Social and Cultural Rights* 1966: § 2.2: 'The
States Parties to the present Covenant undertake to guarantee
the rights enunciated in the present Covenant [which includes
the right to healthcare] will be exercised without discrimination
of any kind as to race, colour, sex, language, religion, political
or other opinion, national or social origin, property, birth or
other status.'

2. Not surprisingly, those who support a social contribution criter-
    ion differ radically among themselves about what should count
    as a contribution or burden, and how this would be gauged
    and balanced. See Kilner: *Who Lives? Who Dies?* 27.

3. An international study of thirty countries concluded that social
    value 'plays a véry significant role in the patient selection pro-
    cess' (R. W. Evans et al., *National Policies for the Treatment of
    End-Stage Renal Disease*. Seattle, WA: Batelle Human Affairs
    Research Centers 1984: 6).

4. Kilner rightly argues that 'throughout the history of medicine,
    social-value selection criteria have generally been condemned
    as unethical . . . Health care has traditionally involved physicians
    in assessing their patients solely with a view toward what will
    benefit the patients themselves. Medical science has stood not
    as the judge of people's merits or value, but as a practice devoted
    to preventing their physical and psychological sufferings. Patient
    selection according to a social-value criterion would radically
    alter that.' (*Who Lives? Who Dies?* 36)

5. United Nations, *International Covenant on Economic, Social and
    Cultural Rights*: § 10.2.

6. Great advances in neonatal intensive care have meant that the
    survival rate for low birthweight infants (1,000 to 1,500 g) is
    now over 95% with long-term neuro-developmental disability
    rates as low as 5% and at a cost per surviving infant of only
    about £10,000. But for very low birthweight babies (under
    1,000 g) the survival rate falls (to about 60%), the impairment

rate rises (up to 14%), and the cost increases substantially (about £70,000 per survivor under 600 g at birth); hence the pressures in recent years to institute a cut-off for intensive care at around the 800 g level on cost-benefit grounds.

7.   United Nations, *International Covenant on Economic, Social and Cultural Rights*: 'The widest possible protection and assistance should be accorded to the family... (2) Special protection should be accorded to mothers... (3) Special measures of protection and assistance should be taken on behalf of all children and young persons... (12)... the right of everyone to the enjoyment of the highest attainable standard of physical and mental health includes (2)(a): The provision for the reduction of the still-birth rate and of infant mortality and for the healthy development of the child.' This is further elaborated in the UN *Convention on the Rights of the Child*.

8.   This supposed policy has achieved legendary status in the literature on healthcare allocation, but no such formal policy seems to exist. Rather the profession seems to have come to a rough consensus and to allow many exceptions. According to some estimates several thousand medically appropriate candidates in Britain are denied dialysis each year due to their age. While the young in Britain (those under 35) have comparable dialysis rates to their counterparts on the Continent, those aged 35 to 64 are significantly less likely to receive dialysis, and those over 64 are only half as likely to be treated. See T. Halper, *The Misfortunes of Others: End-Stage Renal Disease in the United Kingdom*. Cambridge: Cambridge University Press 1989.

9.   A. Bowling, 'Ageism in cardiology'. 319 (1999) *British Medical Journal*: 1353–5.

10. G. Bexell, A. Norberg and B. Norberg, 'Ethical conflicts in long-term care of aged patients'. 7 (1980) *Ethics in Science and Medicine*: 141–145; P. T. Menzel, *Strong Medicine: The Ethical Rationing of Health Care*. Oxford and New York: Oxford University Press 1990: ch. 11; A. Norberg et al., 'Ethical conflicts in long-term care of the aged: nutritional problems and the patient-care worker relationship'. 280 (1980) *British Medical Journal*: 377–8.

11.   See, for general evidence of ageism in healthcare in the NHS: Age Concern, *Turning your back on us*, London: Age Concern England 1999. See further Age Concern's press release of 17 May 2000 on an Age Concern/NOP survey of 200 doctors according to which 'more than three quarters (77 per cent) of GPs claim that age rationing occurs in the NHS, despite Government assurances that treatment is based on clinical need alone'. Half of the doctors (49 per cent) said they would worry about how the NHS would treat them in old age; 43 per cent said they would have concerns about a frail elderly relative going into their local hospital; 33 per cent said elderly patients did not have the same quality of care as other patients; and 16 per cent said older patients had to wait longer for treatment than other patients.

12.   R. Binstock, 'The aged as scapegoat'. 23 (1983) *Gerontologist*: 136–143; R. W. Evans, 'Advanced medical technology and elderly people'. In R. H. Binstock and S. G. Post (eds) *Too Old for Health Care? Controversies in Medicine, Law, Economics and Ethics*. Baltimore and London: Johns Hopkins University Press 1991: 44–74; J. Grimley-Evans, 'Health care rationing and elderly people'. In M. Tunbridge (ed.) *Rationing of Health Care in Medicine*. London: Royal College of Physicians 1993: 43–54; D. H. Taube et al., 'Successful treatment of middle aged and elderly patients with end stage renal disease'. 286 (1983) *British Medical Journal*: 2018–20; R. J. Tesi, 'Renal transplantation in older people'. 343 (1994) *The Lancet*: 461–4; C. J. Winearls, D. O. Oliver and J. Auer, 'Age and dialysis'. 339 (1992) *The Lancet*: 432.

13.   Royal College of Physicians Working Group, 'Report on cardiological interventions in elderly patients'. 25 (1991) *Journal of the Royal College of Physicians*: 197–205; V. Z. Shah et al., 160 (1994) *Medical Journal of Australia*: 332–4.

14.   Grimley-Evans, 'Health care rationing and elderly people': 46.

15.   As Lord Browne-Wilkinson asked (but did not answer) in the *Bland* case at 281: 'If the withdrawal of life support is legitimate in the case of Anthony Bland, whose PVS is very severe, what of others in this country also in PVS (whom we were told

numbered between 1,000 and 1,500) and others suffering from medical conditions having similar impact, e.g. Guillain-Barre syndrome? Who is to decide, and according to what criteria, who is to live and who is to die?'

16. *Euthanasia. Report of the Working Party to review the British Medical Association's guidance on euthanasia.* London: British Medical Association, May 1988.

17. London: British Medical Association, 1999.

18. The BMA uncontroversially hold the provision of 'medical treatment' is only justified if it is in the 'best interests' of a patient. Having controversially classified tubefeeding as 'medical treatment', though its purpose is essentially to sustain life, the BMA clearly take the view that one may judge that it is not in the 'best interests' of severely cognitively impaired patients who are not terminally ill to be tubefed, i.e. it is not in their best interests to be kept alive. Evidently, the underlying judgement is that their *lives* are not worthwhile.

19. The example of the urinary catheter serves to make clear the importance of distinguishing between medical *treatment* (measures requiring medical skills directed to the restoration or maintenance of health, or of some approximation to healthy functioning, or to the palliation of symptoms) and the medical management of *care* (the provision, requiring medical skills, of something ordinarily necessary to sustain any life).

Chapter 13

1. Secretary of State for Health, *The New NHS. Modern – Dependable*: 4.3. London: The Stationery Office, December 1997: 25.

Chapter 14

1. On the notion of the common good see: Aristotle, *Politics* 1252a2; 1284b6; B. J. Diggs, 'The common good as reason for

political action'. 83 (1973) *Ethics*: 283–93; Finnis, *Natural Law and Natural Rights*: 147, 154–155; Grisez, *Living a Christian Life*: 334–8, 345–6.

2. S. Haggard and F. A. Carter, 'Preventing the birth of infants with Down's Syndrome: a cost-benefit analysis'. 1/6012 (1976) *British Medical Journal*: 753–6; S. Haggard, F. A. Carter and R. G. Milne, 'Screening for spina bifida cystica. A cost-benefit analysis', 30 (1976) *British Journal of Preventive and Social Medicine*: 40–53.

3. J. Harris, 'The survival lottery'. 50 (1975) *Philosophy*: 81–7; cf. M. B. Green, 'Harris's modest proposal'. 54 (1979) *Philosophy*: 400–6.

4. See the debate between Illingworth and Bayer: R. Bayer, *Private Acts, Social Consequences*. New York: Macmillan 1989; and R. Bayer, 'AIDS and liberalism: a response to Patricia Illingworth'. 6 (1992) *Bioethics*: 23–7; P. Illingworth, *AIDS and the Good Society*. London: Routledge 1991; P. Illingworth, 'Warning: AIDS health promotion programmes may be hazardous to your autonomy'. In C. Overall and W. Zion (eds) *Perspectives on AIDS: Ethical and Social Issues*. New York: Oxford University Press 1991; P. Illingworth, 'Bayer revisited'. 6 (1992) *Bioethics*: 28–34.

5. The Hippocratic Oath includes the promise: 'I shall never give a deadly drug to anyone who asks for it, nor will I make a suggestion to this effect.' In *R v Cox* (1992) the defendant gave a lethal dose of potassium chloride to a 70-year-old patient who was in severe pain, terminally ill and asked to be killed; he was convicted of attempted murder. Ognall J instructed the jury in these terms: 'The distinction the law requires you to draw is this: Is it proved that in giving the injection in that form and in those amounts Dr Cox's primary purpose was to bring the life of Lillian Boyes to an end? If it was, then he is guilty. If, on the other hand, it was or may have been his primary purpose in acting as he did to alleviate her pain and suffering, then he is not guilty, and that is so even though he recognised that in fulfilling that primary purpose he might or even would hasten the moment of her death... If Dr Cox's primary purpose was to

hasten death it matters not by how much or by how little her death was hastened or intended to be hastened... No doctor can lawfully take any step deliberately to hasten death by however short a period of time.' The case was approved by the Court of Appeal and the House of Lords in *Bland* (1993). Likewise R v *Adams* (1957).

6.   Thus Lord Keith in *Bland* (1993) at 362: 'Where one individual has assumed responsibility for the care of another who cannot look after himself or herself, whether as a medical practitioner or otherwise, that responsibility cannot lawfully be shed... Thus a person having charge of a baby who fails to feed it, so that it dies, will be guilty at least of manslaughter. The same is true of one having charge of an adult who is frail and cannot look after herself.'

7.   Finnis, *Natural Law and Natural Rights*: 107.

8.   See the references at footnotes 10 to 13 of Chapter 12.

9.   J. Finnis, 'Bland: Crossing the Rubicon?'. 109 (1993) *Law Quarterly Review*: 329–37; A. Fisher, 'On not starving the unconscious'. 74 (1993) *New Blackfriars*: 130–45; J. Keown, 'Hard case, bad law, 'new' ethics'. 52 (1993) *Cambridge Law Journal*: 209–12.

10.   See *Bland's Case* (1993) at 339, 357, 381, 397.

11.   House of Lords, Session 1993–94, *Report of the Select Committee on Medical Ethics*. London: HMSO 1994: para. 276.

12.   *Report of the Select Committee on Medical Ethics*: para. 275.

13.   *Report of the Select Committee on Medical Ethics*: para. 276.

14.   This was attempted in a private member's Bill, the *Medical Treatment (Prevention of Euthanasia) Bill*, introduced by Mrs Ann Winterton MP in 1999, which was opposed by the Minister of Health, Yvette Cooper, on behalf of the Government, as well as by the BMA, which lobbied MPs. Unfortunately, the Bill was not given sufficient Parliamentary time for debate.

Chapter 15

1. *Catechism of the Catholic Church* (hereafter *Catechism*) para. 1954; cf. *Catechism* paras. 1954–1960; Finnis, *Natural Law and Natural Rights*.

2. cf. Catholic Health Association of the United States, *No Room in the Marketplace: The Healthcare of the Poor.* St. Louis, MO: The Catholic Health Association 1986, and *idem, With Justice for All? The Ethics of Healthcare Rationing.* St. Louis, MO: The Catholic Health Association 1991; J. M. Finnis and A. Fisher, 'Theology and the four principles: a Roman Catholic view'. In R. Gillon (ed.) *Principles of Health Care Ethics.* Chichester: Wiley 1993: 31–44.

3. Grisez, *Christian Moral Principles*: 115–140, 459–476; cf. Vatican II, *Gaudium et Spes*, paras. 38–39; Pope John Paul II, Encyclical Letter *Solicitudo Rei Socialis* 1987: sec. 47.

4. Finnis & Fisher, 'Theology and the four principles: a Roman Catholic view'.

5. e.g. Pope Leo XIII, Encyclical Letter *Rerum Novarum* 1891; Pope Pius XI, Encyclical Letter *Quadragesinw Anno* 1931; Pope John XXIII, Encyclical Letter *Mater et Magistra* 1961, and Encyclical Letter *Pacem in Terris* 1963; Vatican Council II, *Gaudium et Spes*; Pope Paul VI, Encyclical Letter *Populorum Progressio* 1967, and Apostolic Letter *Octogesima Adveniens* 1971; Synod of Bishops 1971, *Justice in the World;* Pope John Paul II, Encyclical Letter *Laborem Exercens* 1981, Encyclical Letter *Sollicitudo Rei Socialis* 1987, and Encyclical Letter *Centesimus Annus* 1991; National Conference of Catholic Bishops of the USA, *Economic Justice for All: Pastoral Letter on Catholic Social Teaching and the US Economy* 1986. These documents were commonly occasioned by the concerns of their day: the condition of workers; the rise of totalitarian governments; the arms race and threats to world peace; the aspiration to a new international order in which peace is protected and peoples given opportunities to develop; problems with both Marxist and capitalist worldviews. Nonetheless they established some enduring principles. Repudiating approaches which reduce justice to non-interference with

others, or fulfilling agreements, or treating everyone the same, Catholic social teaching has proposed a rich conception of the nature, purposes and obligations of community life, and the need for moral rectitude, fairness and commitment to the common good ('solidarity') among the members of a community.

6. e.g. Congregation for the Doctrine of the Faith *Declaration on Procured Abortion* 1974, *Declaration on Euthansia* 1980, and *Instruction on Respect for Human Life in its Origin and on the Dignity of Procreation* 1987; Pontifical Council for the Pastoral Care of Health Care Workers, *Charter for Health Care Workers* (hereafter *Charter*) 1994; United States Catholic Conference of Bishops, *Ethical and Religious Directives for Catholic Health Services* 1994 (henceforth: USCC, *Ethical and Religious Directives*); Pope John Paul II, Encyclical Letter *Evangelium Vitae* 1995.

7. *Gaudium et Spes*, sec. 29: 'All people are endowed with a rational soul and are created in the image of God; they have the same nature and origin and, being redeemed by Christ, they enjoy the same divine calling and destiny; there is here a basic equality between all persons and it must be given even greater recognition.' On the dignity of the human person: see e.g. *Gaudium et Spes*, Part 1; Vatican Council II, *Dignitatem humanae*.

8. Congregation for the Doctrine of the Faith, *Instruction on respect for human life in its origin and on the dignity of procreation (Donum Vitae)* I, 1987; *Catechism*, paras. 2259ff ; Pope John Paul II, *Evangelium Vitae* 1995.

9. *Catechism*, paras. 2288–91.

10. On the duty of the community to assist the family in caring for the young, the old, the sick, the handicapped, and the poor: *Catechism*, paras. 2208–9.

11. *Charter*, Preface. cf. *Charter*, para. 1, citing *Catechism*, para. 2288 and various addresses by John Paul II: 'The work of health care professionals is a very valuable 'service to life'. It expresses a profoundly human and Christian commitment, undertaken and carried out not only as a technical activity but also as one of dedication to and love of neighbour. It is 'a form of Christian

witness'. 'Their profession calls for them to be guardians and servants of human life.' Life is a primary and fundamental good of the human person. Caring for life, then, expresses, first and foremost, a truly human activity in defence of physical life. It is to this that professional or voluntary health care workers devote their activity.'

12. *Gaudium et Spes*, sec. 25. cf. St. Thomas Aquinas, *Commentary on Aristotle's Nicomachean Ethics* I, 1; *Catechism*, para. 1879.

13. e.g. *Gaudium et Spes*, secs. 24–26, 32: "Scripture teaches us that love of God cannot be separated from love of one's neighbour: 'Any other commandment is summed up in this sentence: You shall love your neighbour as yourself; therefore love is the fulfill-ing of the law' (Rom 13:9–10; cf. 1 Jn 4:20). It goes without saying that this is a matter of the utmost importance to people who are coming to rely more and more on each other... The human person is and ought always to be the beginning, the sub-ject and the object of every social organization... The human person stands above all things and their rights and duties are uni-versal and inviolable... The social order and its development must constantly yield to the good of the person, since the order of things must be subordinate to the order of persons and not *vice versa*... God did not create humankind to live as individuals but to come together in the formation of social unity... In his preaching Christ clearly outlined an obligation on the part of the children of God to treat each other as brothers and sisters. In his prayer he asked that all his followers should be 'one'... This solidarity must be constantly increased until that day when it will be brought to fulfilment..." *Catechism*, para. 1880: "A society is a group of persons bound together organically by a prin-ciple of unity that goes beyond each one of them... By means of society, each man is established as an 'heir' and receives certain 'talents' that enrich his identity and whose fruits he must develop. He rightly owes loyalty to the communities of which he is part, and respect to those in authority who have charge of the common good." On friendship, community or solidarity as a direct demand of human and Christian brotherhood see Pope John Paul II *Sollicitudo Rei Socialis* (1987) and *Centesimus Annus* (1991); *Catechism*, paras. 1939ff. On the necessity of the state for human flourishing: *Catechism*, para. 1882.

14.   *Gaudium et Spes*, sec. 30.

15.   *Gaudium et Spes*, sec. 27; cf. *Catechism*, para. 1931.

16.   *Charter*, para. 4.

17.   This paragraph is drawn from Anthony Fisher OP, 'Is there a distinctive role for the Catholic hospital in a pluralist society?'. In L. Gormally (ed.) *Issues for a Catholic Bioethic*. London: The Linacre Centre 1999: 200–229, at pp. 212–213.

18.   *Charter*, para. 4, quoting from a 1980 address by Pope John Paul II: "What a stimulus for the desired 'personalization' of medicine could come from Christian charity, which makes it possible to see in the features of every sick person the adorable face of the great, mysterious Patient, who continues to suffer in those over whom your profession bends, wisely and providently!"

19.   cf. USCC, *Ethical and Religious Directives*, 1994.

20.   USCC, *Ethical and Religious Directives*.

21.   *Gaudium et Spes*, sec. 29.2 'Every form of social or cultural discrimination in fundamental personal rights on the grounds of sex, race, colour, social conditions, language or religion, must be curbed and eradicated as incompatible with God's design.' On the scandalous and sinful nature of some inequalities of access see: *ibid*, sec. 29.3; *Catechism*, para. 1938.

22.   *Charter*, para. 5.

23.   Against the cult or idolisation of the body and of physical health see: *Gaudium et Spes*, sec. 41; *Catechism*, para. 2289.

24.   The virtue of temperance ought to moderate the consumption of medicine as of other goods: cf. *Catechism*, paras. 1809, 2290, 2407.

25.   See *Charter*, paras. 53–55; Pope John Paul II, Apostolic Letter *On Suffering (Salvifici Doloris)* 1984. See also D. A. Jones OP, 'The encounter with suffering in the practice of medicine in

the light of Christian revelation'. In L. Gormally (ed.) *Issues for a Catholic Bioethic*. London: The Linacre Centre 1999: 159–172.

26. Pope John Paul II, *Evangelium Vitae*, sec. 50.

27. cf. *Charter*, para. 54.

28. *Catechism*, paras. 2213, 2407, 2443ff.

29. Pope John XXIII, *Pacem in Terris*, sec. 11.

30. John Paul II, Homily at Mass in Recife, Brazil, 4 August 1980, in 72 (1980) *Acta Apostolicae Sedis*: 929.

31. *Catechism*, paras. 1908, 2211, 2288.2.

32. United States Catholic Conference, *Health and Healthcare: A Pastoral Letter of the American Bishops*. Washington, DC: United States Catholic Conference 1981. 11 (1981) *Origins*: 396–402.

33. Pope John Paul II, *Centesimus Annus*, sec. 57; Congregation for the Doctrine of the Faith, *Instruction on Christian Freedom and Liberation* 1986, sec. 68; *Catechism*, secs. 2443ff.

34. cf. Mt 5:42; 6:2–4; 8:20; 10:8; 25:31–46; Mk 12:41–44; Lk 3:11; 6:20–22; 11:41; Eph 4:28; Heb 13:3; Jas 2:15–16; 5:1–6; 1 Jn 3:17.

35. cf. *Catechism*, para. 1932.

36. See, e.g. the texts from St. John Chrysostom and St. Gregory the Great cited in *Catechism*, para. 2446.

37. USCC, *Ethical and Religious Directives* 1994. cf. Catholic Health Association, *With Justice for All? The Ethics of Health Care Rationing*, p. 24: 'Those who are marginalized by society – those who cannot speak for themselves, the powerless, the disenfranchised, the vulnerable – have the most urgent claim on healthcare because they are among the least fortunate in our society. Rationing schemes should not be devised to the detriment of these people. Given the life-threatening conditions in which

they are often forced to live, their claims on the healthcare system are ethically more compelling, not less. Development of healthcare policy should always proceed from the perspective of disadvantaged persons, with a bias toward improving their health status first.'

38. e.g. *Gaudium et Spes*, sec. 27; John Paul II, *Salvifici Doloris*, 1981; John Paul II, *Christifideles Laici*, 1988: sec. 48; John Paul II, 'Letter to the elderly', *L'Osservatore Romano* 1 October 1999.

39. Ex 20:12; Dt 5:16; cf. Lk 2:51; Mk 7:8–13; Eph 6:1–3; *Catechism*, paras. 2197ff.

40. Pope John Paul II, *Evangelium Vitae*, sec. 94; cf. Pontifical Council for the Laity, *The Dignity of Older People and their Mission in the Church and in the World* in *L'Osservatore Romano* [weekly edition] 10 February 1999.

41. *Catechism*, para. 1936.

42. e.g. Pope John XXIII, *Mater et Magistra; Gaudium et Spes*, secs. 26.1 and 74.1; Pope Paul VI *Populorum Progressio*; United States Catholic Conference of Bishops, *Economic Justice for All. Catholic Social Teaching and the US Economy* 1986, sec. 8; and *Catechism*, paras. 1905–6: the common good is 'the sum total of social conditions which allow people, either as groups or as individuals, to reach their fulfilment more fully and more easily'. Vatican Council II, *Dignitatis Humanae*, sec. 6: 'The common good of society consists in the sum total of those conditions of social life which enable people to achieve a fuller measure of perfection with greater ease.' cf. USCC, *Ethical and Religious Directives*, 1994.

43. *Catechism*, paras. 2240 and 2465 (cf. Mt 22:21; Rom 13:7).

44. *Catechism*, para. 1880.

45. *Dignitatis Humanae*, sec. 3: 'Since the common welfare of society consists in the entirety of those conditions of social life under which people enjoy the possibility of achieving their own perfection in a certain fullness of measure and also with some relative

ease, it chiefly consists in the protection of the rights, and in the performance of the duties, of the human person.'

46. *Gaudium et Spes*, sec. 26: 'The common good is the sum total of social conditions which allow people, either as groups or as individuals, to reach their fulfilment more fully and more easily ... The human person ought to have ready access to all that is necessary for living a genuinely human life: for example, food, clothing, housing ... The social order requires constant improvement: it must be founded in truth, built on justice, and enlivened by love: it should grow in freedom towards a more humane equilibrium.'

47. cf. *Catechism*, paras. 1942 and 2447.

48. Catholic Health Association, *With Justice for All? The Ethics of Health Care Rationing*, pp. 15–16: "The common good cannot be reduced simply to the will of the majority, and it is not synonymous with 'the greatest good for the greatest number'. Rather, the common good is achieved when communities of mutual concern and responsibility work on behalf of all. In healthcare, the common good is an ideal that presupposes initiatives from all sectors of society, including healthcare providers, the insurance industry, and government. In practice, the common good calls for solidarity, that is, an ethical commitment to do whatever is necessary to create constructive forms of social, political and economic interdependence."

49. cf. *Catechism*, paras. 1939 and 2407.

50. *Catechism*, para. 2446.

51. *Gaudium et Spes*, sec. 69; here the Council cites St. Basil, Lactantius, St. Augustine, St. Gregory the Great, St. Bonaventure and St. Albert the Great. See also: St. Thomas Aquinas, *Summa Theologiae* IIa IIae 32, 5; 66, 2; Pope Leo XIII, *Rerum Novarum*; Pope John XXIII, *Mater et Magistra*; Pope John Paul II, *Sollicitudo Rei Socialis* and *Centesimus Annus; Catechism*, paras. 2402ff.

52. *Gaudium et Spes*, sec. 29; cf. sec. 63.

53. *Gaudium et Spes*, sec. 66.

54. On the inadequacy of profitability and efficiency tests of the appropriate use of property see: Pope John Paul II, *Centesimus Annus*: sec. 24; *Catechism*, paras. 2423–25.

55. The United States Bishops (*Ethical and Religious Directives*) make the point that this applies to Catholic health care institutions, especially hospitals. 'Catholic health care ministry exercises responsible stewardship of available health care resources. A just health care system will be concerned both with promoting equity of care – to assure that the right of each person to basic health care is respected – and with promoting the good health of all in the community. The responsible stewardship of health care resources can be accomplished best in dialogue with people from all levels of society, in accordance with the principle of subsidiarity and with respect for the moral principles which guide institutions and persons.'

56. e.g. Pope John Paul II, *Evangelium Vitae*, sec. 26: 'a just international distribution of medical resources is still far from being a reality'.

57. 'The benefits provided in national healthcare policy should be sufficient to maintain and promote good health as well as treat disease and disability. Emphasis should be placed on the promotion of health, the prevention of disease, and adequate protection against environmental and other hazards to physical and mental health. If health is viewed in an integrated and comprehensive manner, the social and economic context of illness and healthcare must be an important focus of concern and action... Public policy should provide incentives for preventive care, early intervention and alternative delivery systems.' (United States Catholic Conference of Bishops, *Pastoral Letter on Health and Healthcare*. Washington, DC: United States Catholic Conference 1981.)

58. *Catechism*, paras. 1883, 2208–09; Pope Pius XI, *Quadragesimo Anno*; Pope John XXIII, *Mater et Magistra*, sec. 53. cf. Boyle, 'The concept of health and the right to health care'; Finnis, *Natural Law and Natural Rights*: 146–147, 168–169; Grisez, *Living a Christian Life*: 847–848. In this respect Catholic teaching sympathizes with liberal suspicion of creeping bureaucracy and

hostility toward attempts to regulate all of human society by government.

59. Pope John Paul II, *Centesimus Annus*, sec. 48.4.

60. *Gaudium et Spes*, sec. 27.

61. Examples of recent texts include: Pope John Paul II 1995, *Evangelium Vitae*, sec. 27; *Charter*, paras. 3, 5.

62. *Charter*, para. 3, citing Pope John Paul II, Address to the Association of Catholic Doctors, 28 December 1978 (*Insegnamenti* 1: 436) and Discourse for the 120th Anniversary of the Bambini Gesu Hospital, 18 March 1989 (*Insegnamenti* XII/1: 605–8, sec. 2).

63. *Catechism*, para. 2257.

64. *Charter*, paras. 50–52.

Chapter 16

1. Catholic Health Association, *With Justice for All? The Ethics of Health Care Rationing*: 21. Boyle, 'The right to health care and its limits': 23, suggests that 'priority will be given to providing the basic care children need to get a decent start in life, to similar help for those who because of poverty or other deprivation cannot provide for their own healthcare, and to first contact care, diagnosis, and pain control for everybody. These are minimally the relatively simple things which decent people would want for themselves and seek for their dependents and neighbours, and which the healthcare system can surely facilitate their providing. These services should, I think, take priority in healthcare over more exotic treatments for those who can take for granted such minimally adequate healthcare.'

2. Calman, 'Decision making and the National Health Service: making choices in the real world – a philosophical approach': 29, argues that primary care would include 'child health, maternity services, care of the elderly and community care, [would] provide individuals and families with a front-line service to deal with the

majority of illnesses, and [would] ensure that health promotional efforts are delivered.' Emergency services would include 'a trauma service, and facilities for dealing with emergency problems and acute life-saving issues such as heart attacks'.

3.   The proportion of GDP which various developed countries spend on healthcare varies significantly. The latest figures from the World Health Organization (June 2000) show the United States spending 13.7%, Germany 10.5%, Switzerland 10.1%, France 9.8%, Italy 9.3%, Sweden 9.2%, Netherlands 8.8%, Portugal 8.2%, Belgium 8.0%, Denmark 8.0%, Spain 8.0%, Ireland 6.2%, and the UK 5.8%. But total spending bears little relation to the quality and coverage of healthcare. In the recent WHO league tables, whereas France and Italy are ranked respectively 1st and 2nd, and the UK and Ireland 18th and 19th, Germany is ranked 25th, and the USA 37th! Notoriously in the USA a third of the population has no healthcare coverage, whereas Britain has universal coverage. Mr. Blair's January 2000 pledge to raise total UK healthcare spending by 2006 to match the European Union average as a proportion of GDP (9% in 1997, not 8% as he claimed) would require a 9.7% per annum increase in real terms in NHS spending over five years. (See J. Appleby and S. Boyle, 'Blair's billions: where will he find the money for the NHS?'. 320 (2000) *British Medical Journal*: 865–7.)

4.   R v *Secretary of State for Social Services, ex parte Hincks & Ors.* (1980) 1 *Butterworth's Medico-Legal Reports* 93 at 96.

5.   Following the strict standard set in *Provincial Picture Houses Ltd* v *Wednesbury Corp* (1948) an applicant must show that the decision is such that no reasonable decision-maker would have come to it.

6.   R v *Secretary of State for Social Services (Central Birmingham Area Health Authority), ex parte Walker.* 3 *Butterworth's Medico-Legal Reports* 32.

7.   Re J *(a minor) (child in care: medical treatment).* [1992] 3 *Weekly Law Reports* 507; 4 *All England Law Reports* 614.

8.   R v *Central Birmingham Health Authority, ex parte Collier* (unreported, 6 Jan 1988).

9. R v *Cambridge Health Authority ex parte B.* [1995] 2 *All* E R 129. See also R v *North Derbyshire Health Authority ex parte Fisher.* 8 (1997) *Medical Law Review*: 237.

10. R v *Cambridge Health Authority ex parte B.* [1995] 2 *All* E R 129 at 137.

11. *Ibid.*, at 136.

12. *Ibid.*, at 137.

13. *Ibid.*, at 137.

14. [1999] *Lloyd's Law Reports Medical* 399.

15. See note 5 above.

16. *Ibid.*, at 411.

17. *Ibid.*, at 413.

18. *Ibid.*, at 410 *per* Auld LJ.

19. See (1990) 41 *Butterworth's Medico-Legal Reports* 171.

20. *Wilsher* v *Essex Area Health Authority.* [1986] 3 *All England Law Reports* 801; [1987] *Queen's Bench* 730.

21. *Bull* v *Devon Area Health Authority.* 4 (1993) *Medical Law Review*: 117.

22. *Knight* v *Home Office.* [1990] 3 *All England Law Reports* 237; 4 *Butterworth's Medico-Legal Reports* 85.

23. British Medical Association, *Withholding and Withdrawing Life-prolonging Medical Treatment. Guidance for decision making.* London: BMJ Books 1999: sec. 21.4 (pp. 56–7).

24. House of Lords, Session 1993–94, *Report of the Select Committee on Medical Ethics*, Volume I, Report, para. 275.

Index

abandonment of patients, 118, 142; norm
  against, 65, 79, 101, 120, 188
abortion, 42, 47, 65, 87, 133, 136, 186
access to healthcare, 158, 165, 166, 167,
  189
action, reasons for. *See* reasons for
  choice/action
ad hoc allocation, 22–27
administrative costs, 167, 189
age, 20, 39; and selection for treatment,
  116–119, 175, 180, 189, 212n.8
age discrimination. *See* elderly, treatment
  of
aggregation of preferences, 66
AIDS, 10, 58, 67
allocation, concept of, 7
allocation of healthcare resources, 7,
  13–16, 18, 25–35 *passim*, 65, 69, 85,
  88, 152–153, 157, 189; criteria for,
  102, 107–108, 109–132 *passim*,
  174–175; decision-making, 177–180,
  191; defective approaches to (*see*:
  consensus principles of allocation;
  deserts, allocation by; free market;
  liberal-welfarism; neutral principles
  of allocation; principlist approach to
  allocation; utilitarian approaches to
  allocation); levels of system it occurs
  at, 8, 166; unsystematic approaches
  to, 25–35 *passim*
Alzheimer's disease, 10
America. *See* U.S.A.
antenatal care, 65
assisted nutrition and hydration. *See*
  tubefeeding

asthma, 10, 58
autonomy, ideal of, 47–49, 78, 123;
  respect for, 41, 42, 45, 47–49, 66,
  99

basic care, 121–123; duty to provide, 122
basic goods, 46, 60, 65, 71, 75, 76–81
  passim, 84, 85, 92, 93, 98, 105, 106,
  133, 160, 185–186. *See also* human
  good(s)
basic human needs. *See* needs, basic
  human
basic human rights. *See* rights, basic
basic services, 165
basic social goods, 51, 134–135
basic values. *See* basic goods; human
  good(s)
beneficial treatment. *See* treatment,
  beneficial
benefits, healthcare, 59, 119, 128;
  identification of, 55, 58–59, 60, 66;
  quality of life, 55, 58
benevolence, 68, 130
'better off dead'. *See* life: 'not worth
  living'
Beveridge Report, 46
biased allocation, 50–51, 66–67, 111, 139
Bible, The, 96
Bland Case, 133, 140–142, 173–174, 190.
  See also British Medical Association;
  euthanasia; intentional killing by
  planned omission; starving patients;
  tubefeeding; unconscious patients;
  withdrawing/withholding care;
  withdrawing/withholding treatment

bodily existence. *See* human person, conceptions of

bodily integrity: respect for, 66, 133; right to, 151, 190

brain damage, irreversible, 122, 173. *See also* consciousness, level of

British Medical Association, The, 116, 121–123, 140–141; *Euthanasia* (1988 Report of), 121; *Withholding and Withdrawing Lifeprolonging Medical Treatment* (1999 Ethics Committee Report of), 121–123, 141, 173–174, 214nn.18, 19

burdensome treatment. *See* treatment, burdensome

bureaucracy (healthcare), 33, 69, 157, 180

calculus of benefits, 63

cancer, 8, 10; treatment of, 116

cardinal measurement of benefits. *See* commensurating: benefits and losses

cardiology, 116

care: positive duty of, 137–138, 188, 208n.5, 216n.6; standard of, 165

Catholic bioethical teaching, 19, 146–161 *passim*

Catholic Church and healthcare, xii, 21–22, 146

Catholic social teaching, 19, 21, 145–161

causation of disease/damage to health, 124, 138

charity, 20, 42, 112, 188

childbirth, 11

choice: and character, 64, 68, 78, 205n.20; freedom of, 111; reasons for, *see* reasons for choice/action

Christian healthcare, 159

chronic ailments, 51

chronic care, 10, 58

chronically ill patients, 65, 67, 139, 142

clinical audit, 14

comfort, 60, 122–123

commensurating: benefits and losses, 61, 63–64; values, 55

commissioning, 40

common good, 19, 25, 42, 46, 48, 73, 79, 80, 91, 96, 105, 106, 111, 114, 133, 134–135, 136, 137, 147, 154, 156, 157, 187, 222n.42, 222–223n.45, 223nn.46, 48

common law, 22, 95, 174

common morality, norms of, 19, 22, 65, 66, 79, 137, 145 *See also* moral norms

communitarianism, 74, 93

community, conceptions of, 73, 91, 92–94, 106, 145, 146, 147, 148, 187. *See also* common good

community responsibility for healthcare. *See* social responsibility for healthcare

community services, 12

comprehensive healthcare, 10, 46, 165, 168; and NHS ideal, 166, 189

compulsory treatments, 47

conceptions of the good (life). *See* human good

conscientious objection, 47, 99

consciousness, level of: and quality of life, 20, 39, 60, 122; and selection for treatment, 119–123, 189, 190

consensus principles of allocation, 37, 40–41, 184

consent, 65, 137. *See also* informed consent

consequentialism, 42, 99

Conservative Government, 12

contraception, 87

controlled trials, 62

cooperation in healthcare, 91, 92–102 *passim*, 147, 187

coronary disease, 8, 10

cosmetic treatments, 6, 57, 87

cost-benefit analysis, 18, 57, 60, 69, 99–100, 130, 158

cost: containment, 179; cutting, 141; effectiveness, 59, 60, 69–70; efficiency, 136

costing procedures, 69

courts, 167–173 *passim*

culture, 92, 102

culture of death, 147

cultural prejudice, 40

custodial care, 65

death: as benefit, 60; meaning of, 150

debate, need for, 102, 167, 180–181
Declaration of Geneva, 104
defensive medicine, 11, 194n.5
demand for healthcare, 11, 15
democratic decision-making, 41
democratic state and conceptions of good
    life, 39. *See also* value neutrality of
    the state
depression, 11
desert, allocation by, 108, 114–125 *passim*
desire-satisfaction, 86–88. *See also*
    healthcare need; healthcare,
    spurious
dialysis, 11, 57, 116, 131, 212n.8
dignity, human, 60, 66, 77, 79, 96, 97, 98,
    100, 111, 118, 120, 130, 142, 145,
    146, 151, 156; inalienable, 147
disability, 11, 127, 128, 142
disadvantaged, 46, 51, 52–53, 57, 67, 98,
    110, 112, 114, 120
discounted future earnings, 62
discrimination, unjust, 18, 51, 99,
    111–112, 120, 140, 159, 167, 174,
    190, 220n.21. *See also* biased
    allocations
distributable goods, 46
doctor-patient relationship, 17, 48, 105,
    113, 178; understood as contractual,
    28, 29, 48; understood as fiduciary,
    48
dualism. *See* human person, conceptions
    of
duties, 83, 88–89, 91, 92, 101, 103, 106,
    147, 155, 186–187. *See also* moral
    norms
duties of Secretary of State, 168
duty of care, common, 94, 95, 158. *See*
    also Good Samaritanism
duty, statutory, 169
dying patients, 65, 67, 117, 127, 130. *See*
    also palliative care; terminally ill
    patients

effectiveness of healthcare, 59, 68, 69, 87,
    127, 130, 146, 185, 189
efficiency, 14–15, 47, 69–70, 79, 81, 89,
    98–99, 105, 127, 130, 136, 146, 156,
    179, 185, 189

elderly, injustice to, 174
elderly, neglect of frail, 133, 139–140,
    174, 190; in NHS, 142
elderly, respect for, 100, 118–119;
    Catholic teaching on, 153
elderly, treatment of, 11, 15, 65, 67, 190;
    discrimination in, 116–119, 130, 173,
    190, 213n.11; legislation against
    discrimination in, 173, 190
embryo experimentation, 133, 136, 190
emergency care, 28
emergency services, 165, 189
ends of healthcare. *See* healthcare, ends/
    goals of
enhancement treatments, 6
equal access, 51, 107
equal respect/concern, 52, 68, 118, 120,
    130
equal worth of persons, 27, 98, 100. *See*
    also dignity, human
equality, 20, 39, 46, 49–51, 100, 120; and
    allocation of healthcare, 109–112; of
    access, 127, 189; of opportunity, 45;
    of persons, 46, 79, 96
equity, xvi, 20, 156
ethnicity, 65
eugenics, 6
euthanasia, 43, 47, 87, 118, 136, 141,
    173–174; attitude of UK
    Government to, 174. *See also*
    intentional killing by planned
    omission
exercisable abilities, 60, 119–120
experimentation, detrimental, 136
extraordinary treatment. *See* treatment,
    extraordinary

fairness, 66, 80, 92, 98, 140, 155, 187. *See*
    also Golden Rule
family, 15, 91, 100, 115–116, 118,
    208nn.3, 4; limitation, 65;
    responsibility for healthcare, 94–95,
    106, 176, 187
fertility regulation, 6
first come, first served, 50–51, 110–111,
    130
fraternity, ideal/principle of, 45, 46,
    51

free market (in healthcare), 17–18, 20, 26, 27–35, 96, 102, 107, 112–113, 184; rights of healthworkers in, 28–30; rights of patients in, 32; role of state in, 32–33; rights of taxpayers in, 30–32
freedom, 48. *See also* liberty
friendship, good of, 67, 95
futile treatment. *See* treatment, futile

gatekeeping, 177–180. *See also* General Practitioners as gatekeepers
gender re-assignment. *See* 'sex-change' operations
General Practitioners, 10, 179; as gatekeepers, 7, 178–179; as fundholders, 12. *See also* Primary Care Groups/Trusts
generosity, 68
geriatric patients. *See* elderly, treatment of
Golden Rule, 79, 98, 101, 111, 139, 151, 155, 174, 179, 209nn.8, 9. *See also* fairness
goods. *See* human goods
Good Samaritanism, 67–68, 95, 96, 104, 112, 113, 114, 125, 149, 158–160. *See also* duty of care, common
government, purpose of, 134–135. *See also* political society, end of

haemodialysis. *See* dialysis
handicapped, 65, 67, 116, 120, 130; neglect of, 139–140, 142
happiness. *See* human flourishing
harm, 68, 85, 87, 88
harming, norm against, 79, 94, 99, 101, 120, 137
health: as ability to function socially, 4–5; basic good of, 67, 75, 76–78, 84, 93, 95, 97, 119, 150, 186; biomedical/organic understanding of, 5, 77, 83, 188; gain, 59, 60, 65, 130, 179, 204n.14; indices, 59; profiles, 62–63; promotion, 65, 68, 69, 77, 86, 120; restoration of, 6, 188; status, 59, 123; WHO definition of, 4, 193nn.1, 3
health authorities, 8, 12, 123, 128, 131, 157, 168–172 *passim*, 176

health system: one-tiered, 110; two-tiered, 51
healthcare: appropriate, 85; as social good, 95–97; as social product, 29–30, 98, 113; benefits (*see* benefits, healthcare; benefits, quality of life); costs, 11, 14, 16, 17; determining level of, 78; distribution of, 97–98; duty to provide, 91–102 *passim*; ends/goals of, 5–6, 59, 188 (*see also* palliation of symptoms; prolongation of life; restoration of health); entitlements to, 102, 151; expenditure, 14; limitations of, 150; minimum level of, 102; practice, 188 (*see also*: medical practice; nursing practice; professional conduct; professional duties); provision of, government/private mix in, 175–176; responsibilities for, 89–90, 94–98 (*see also*: family, responsibility for healthcare; personal responsibility for health; social responsibility for health); social expectations of, 11, 87–88; spurious, 83, 86–88, 127, 186; technologies, 65; understanding of, 3, 5–6, 73, 103–105; universal access to, 102; vocation to, 17, 77–78, 103. *See also* comprehensive healthcare; demand for healthcare; universal healthcover
healthcare budget: allocation of, *see* allocation of healthcare resources, criteria for; total, 8, 165–167
healthcare need, 10, 50, 51, 83, 84–86, 87–88, 89–90, 91, 98, 127–128, 130, 131, 132, 186, 190; allocation by, 108, 111, 115, 127–131, 158, 189; assessment of, 160
healthcare resources: constituent factors in, 6–7; total, 165–167, 189; use of, 14–15, 69, 80–81, 98, 123, 130, 131, 156
healthcare spending as percentage of GDP, 10, 165–167, 226n.3
healthcare system, 7, 94, 96, 100, 106, 165; core values of, 103–105, 134; purpose of, xvi

hierarchies of goods/values, 63, 77, 101, 154, 175
hip replacement, 57, 58, 62, 63
Hippocratic: ethic, 10, 179; oath, 22, 104, 215–216n.5; tradition, 50, 73, 79, 178
HIV, compulsory screening for, 136
homicidal/harmful healthcare allocation: direct, 136–137, 141, 147; indirect, 137–138
hospital-based services, 165, 189
House of Lords Select Committee on Medical Ethics (1993–94), 177
human association, atomistic views of, 91, 93, 187. See also individualism
human being, nature of. See human person, conceptions of
human flourishing, 4, 25, 34, 48–49, 58, 66, 71, 75–81 passim, 85, 91, 93, 96, 97, 102, 105, 111, 123, 134, 147, 151, 154, 185–187 passim
human good(s), 38, 39, 40, 45, 49, 51, 73, 75–81 passim, 85, 93, 102, 106, 134, 158. See also basic goods
human life, respect for, 42, 66, 77, 80, 104, 122, 147, 188. See also dignity, human
human person: conceptions of, 39, 49, 73, 77, 83–84, 93, 106, 145, 146, 186–187, 206n.1; respect for, 127. See also human life, respect for
human rights, respect for, 46, 80. See also right to life; right to treatment; rights
human well-being. See human flourishing

ill-health, 96
impartiality, 39, 98, 137, 139
incapacitated patients, 65
inclusiveness, 158
incommensurability (of goods), 63, 75, 99, 205n.1. See also basic good(s)
individualism, 43, 93, 94, 105, 148
inequality, 46, 50–51, 110–111, 156
inequities in healthcare, 18
infant mortality, 59
infertility, 10; treatment for, 3, 57, 58, informed consent, 47

injustices (in healthcare allocation and practice), 21. See also abandonment of patients; abortion; age and selection for treatment; biased allocation; British Medical Association; discrimination, unjust; elderly, injustice to; elderly, neglect of frail; elderly, treatment of; embryo experimentation; euthanasia; handicapped, neglect of; homicidal/harmful healthcare allocation; inequities in healthcare; intentional killing by planned omission; killing of patients; mentally ill, neglect of; poor; punitive healthcare allocation; quality of life and selection for treatment; right to life; starving patients; withdrawing/withholding care
institutional care, 65. See also chronic care
instrumental goods, 46, 60, 75, 76, 83, 85
integrity, 66
intensive care, 116, 129
intentional killing by planned omission, 121–122, 190. See also tubefeeding, withdrawal of
interpersonal comparisons, 64
intrinsic goods. See basic goods
in vitro fertilisation, 3, 87

Jesus, 146–160 passim; his care for the sick, 148–149, 158; his preferential love for the poor/disadvantaged, 152
Judeo-Christian teaching, 73–74
judicial review, 170
justice, 19–21, 25, 38, 52, 64–67 passim, 69, 80, 92, 100, 101, 102, 104, 113–114, 127, 140, 147, 148, 151, 152, 166, 188; distributive, 20, 92, 97–98, 106, 132, 133, 134, 152, 155, 187; libertarian view of, 28, 34; principlist understanding of, 42

killing of patients, 66, 68, 136, 188. See also abortion; euthanasia; intentional killing by planned omission; starving patients

killing the innocent, norm against, 65, 79, 99, 101, 120, 137, 160, 174, 190
Koran, The, 22, 96

Labour Government, 12, 15
legal entitlements in respect of treatment, 172–173. *See also* right to healthcare/ treatment, legal recognition of
legal rights of patients, 102
legislation, need for, 173–174. *See also*: *Bland* Case; elderly, treatment of
length of life, 65. *See also* life span; prolongation of life
liberal theory, 37–71 *passim*, 119–120, 155–156
liberal welfarism, 38, 45–53, 93, 184–185
libertarian approaches, 27, 28–30. *See also* free market
liberty, 53; principle of, 46, 47–49
life: basic good of, 67, 75, 76–78, 84, 93, 95, 97, 186; chances/opportunities, 50; expectancy, 59, 65, 207n.6; 'not worth living', 60, 119–123 *passim*, 137, 138, 173; span, 117
life-plans, 39, 60, 75, 77, 78, 94, 111
lifesaving treatment, 129
life-style choices, 123, 124
long-term care, 18
lottery, 50–51, 110–111, 130
love, 147, 148; Christian, 150; preferential (for poor, sick, disadvantaged), 152
low birthweight babies, 58, 211–212n.6
lying, norm against, 79, 101, 188

management, 12, 14, 26
marginal benefits, 64, 167, 189
marginal costs, 64
marginalized, the, 147, 221–222n.37. *See also*: abandonment of patients; elderly, neglect of frail; handicapped; poor patients
market, healthcare, 102. *See also* free market
markets: external, 27; internal, 27
marriage relationship, 91. *See also* family
maternity care, 58
medical care, 79, 96, 102; right to, 151
medical education, 155

medical ethics, 105, 111, 120; codes of, 137
medical knowledge as social product, 29–30, 98
medical paternalism, 47
medical practice, 94
medical resources, misuse of, 4
medical specialisation, 9
medical technology, 9
medical treatment, 122, 140, 141. *See also* treatment
Medicare, 57
medicalization, tendency to, 4, 11, 87, 104
medicine, high-tech, 10, 117; profession of, 77. *See also* profession, character of
mental ability. *See*: consciousness, level of; exercisable abilities
mental disability, 153
mentally ill, 139, 190; neglect of, 139–140
mentally impaired. *See* consciousness, level of
mercy, 67, 69, 80, 125, 148, 152
moderation, virtue of, 80, 89
monopoly, 29, 30, 33
moral dilemmas, 42
moral dispositions, 4. *See also* virtues, moral
moral norms, 79–80, 89, 92, 97, 103, 120, 158; negative and positive, 75, 79, 94, 101, 103, 174–175, 186. *See also* moral principles
moral principles, 15, 18, 38, 106, 120, 160
mutilation, 133, 136, 190. *See also* bodily integrity; 'sex-change' operations; sterilization

National Health Service, 7, 10, 27, 45, 46, 94, 96, 102, 107, 110, 116, 127, 157, 166, 178, 180, 187; Executive, 12; failures of care in, xv, 116, 142; misallocation of resources in, 18; *National Health Service Act* (1977), 168; purchaser/provider split in, 12, 16, 176; reforms in, 12, 14, 176; *The New NHS* (1997), 127
natural law, 21, 51, 74, 158

natural resources, 31–32, 33
need for healthcare. *See* healthcare need
needs, 20, 25, 66, 78–79, 83, 84–90
    passim, 97, 147, 148, 166; basic
    human, 46, 78–79, 83, 84–86, 96,
    186; claims, limits to, 86–89, 128;
    local, 176; ranking of, 90
neighbourliness, good, 149, 159. *See also*
    Good Samaritanism
neonatal care, 58, 65, 190
neutral principles of allocation, 37,
    38–40, 46, 184
neutrality. *See* liberal theory; value
    neutrality of the state
noninterference rights, 33
nonmaleficence, 41
nursing care, 79, 96, 102, 117, 119
nursing practice, 94
nursing, profession of, 77, 188. *See also*
    profession, character of

oligopoly, 29
opinion polls, 40–41. *See also* polling
opportunities: equal, 49–51 (*see also*
    equality); normal range of, 49–50,
    52, 53
opportunity costs, 15, 166
Oregon Scheme, 16, 40, 41, 56, 57–58,
    59, 62, 66, 69
organs for transplant, allocation and
    supply of, 13, 34, 65, 129, 136
original position, 39–40
outcomes research, 69

pacemaker implantation, 57
pain, 11, 128, 150
palliative care, 58, 117, 119, 122
palliation of symptoms, 6, 188. *See also*
    healthcare: ends/goals of
paternalism, governmental, 33, 123, 157,
    176. *See also* medical paternalism
patient autonomy, 47. *See also* autonomy,
    ideal of
patient charters, 99
persistent vegetative state (PVS), 122;
    patients in, 140–141; *See also*
    consciousness, level of; starving
    patients; tubefeeding

personal responsibility for health, 20, 33,
    47, 69, 83, 89–90, 92, 106, 186–187;
    and selection for treatment, 123–125,
    138–139; inalienable character of,
    147
piety, 118
plans of life. *See* life-plans
pleasures (and pains), 58, 60
pluralist society, 38
plurality of goods, 66, 75
political society, end of, 97. *See also*
    government, purpose of
polling, 40, 51, 63, 69
poor: neglect of, 139–140, 142; option
    for, 152–153, 158; treatment of, 15,
    17, 190
practical wisdom, 104
preferences, 58, 93, 103, 112; laundering
    of, 58, 66; satisfaction of, 58, 59, 105
preferential treatment, 113; for those with
    dependents, 115; for the young,
    115–119
prejudiced allocation. *See* biased
    allocation
preventive measures, 34, 58, 59
price mechanism, 112
primary care, 10, 12, 165, 189,
    225–226n.2
Primary Care Groups/Trusts, 12, 157,
    179, 195n.8
principles of allocation, basis for, 38–43,
    73–106. *See also* allocation of
    healthcare resources
principlist approach to allocation, 37, 38,
    41–43, 184
prioritization, 127–131, 176. *See also*
    rationing
private healthcare, 12, 111, 176
private insurance, 11, 27, 33, 113
private property, 31–32, 155–156,
    197nn.5, 6
private treatment, 12
privatisation of health services, 14, 17
profession, character of, 29, 66, 68, 92,
    96, 103
professional autonomy, 26, 47
professional conduct, codes of, 99, 102,
    103–104

professional duties, 17, 101, 125, 155; of
care, 172. *See also* duty of care
profit: margins, 167, 189; maximization,
29
prolongation of life, 59, 60, 64, 77. *See
also* healthcare: ends/goals of
promises, duty to keep, 42
psychiatric care, 67
psychometric index, 56
public expenditure, 14
public health, 165, 189
public policy, 165–181 *passim*
punitive healthcare allocations, 99,
138–139, 159
purchasers of healthcare, 12. *See also*
National Health Service, purchaser/
provider split in
PVS patients. *See* persistent vegetative
state

Quality Adjusted Life Years (QALYs),
16, 40, 56–57, 59, 63–67
QALY: benefits/gains, 56–57, 68, 130,
159, 179, 185; studies, 40, 41, 56–57;
theories, 61, 63
quality of life, 20, 41, 55, 58, 60, 61, 65,
66, 120, 174; and selection for
treatment, 119–123, 130, 133, 175,
189; benefits. *See* benefits, quality of
life
quality of well-being scale, 57
queuing, 11, 15, 26, 50–51, 165. *See also*
first come, first served

ranking of needs. *See* needs, ranking of
ranking (ordinal) of values/benefits, 55,
62, 63
rational deliberation, 76
rational soul, 84, 218n.7
rationing: concept of, 7; explicit, 7, 8,
16, 57–58, 61; implicit, 7,
178–179; levels of system it occurs
at, 8
reasons for choice/action, 75, 76, 78, 88,
90, 92, 99
reproductive liberty, 47
rescue, 67–68, 96, 158
resources, distribution of, 97–98,

166–167. *See also* healthcare
resources, use of
respect for human life. *See* human life,
respect for
responsible stewardship, 156
restoration of health, 59, 60. *See also*
healthcare: ends/goals of
reverence for life. *See* human life, respect
for
right to healthcare/treatment, 11, 17, 28,
92, 100–102, 106, 136, 151–152, 153,
167–168, 225n.1; legal recognition
of, 167–173 *passim*, 190
right to life, 136, 151, 153; actions
contrary to, 190; resource allocation
contrary to, 133. *See also*: abortion;
euthanasia; intentional killing by
planned omission; starving patients
rights, 100–101, 133, 146, 147, 187; as
trumps, 101; basic, 133, 136, 154,
190; civil, 147; claims, 106; prima
facie, 101; rhetoric of, 210n.11
risks: behavioural (to health), 123–125; to
life and health, 128
Royal Colleges, Medical, 94
Royal College of Nursing, 94
rule utilitarianism, 66

sanctity of human life, 68, 100, 112, 151.
See also killing the innocent, norm
against
saving lives, 59, 136, 138, 188
scarcity of resources, 13–16, 65
secondary healthcare, 16
self-determination. *See* autonomy, ideal of
self-inflicted injuries, 124, 138
self-neglect, 123–124
self-ownership, 29, 30
senile dementia, advanced, 122, 142, 173.
See also British Medical Association;
consciousness, level of
'sex-change' operations, 6, 87, 136,
170–172. *See also* bodily integrity,
respect for; mutilation
sex selection, 87
sexual abuse, norm against, 79
sexually transmitted diseases, 10, 124, 125
skill in work, good of, 77

smoking, 57, 124

social contribution/value (of an individual), 20, 65, 108; and selection for treatment, 113–114, 130, 159, 175, 189, 211nn.3, 4

social cooperation, 91, 96–97

social goals (competing for resources with healthcare), 134–135, 166

social organization, levels of, 91, 187

social provision of healthcare, 96, 187. *See also* healthcare: provision of

social responsibility for healthcare, 28, 95–97, 106, 141, 153–155

society, character of, 68, 121, 134–135, 155. *See also* political society, end of

solidarity, 46, 50, 51, 105, 111, 113, 118, 125, 130, 140, 154, 155, 188, 189, 190

starving patients, 121–122, 133, 174, 190, 208n.5. *See also* tubefeeding, withdrawal of

sterilization, 87, 133, 136, 190. *See also*: bodily integrity, respect for; mutilation

subsidiarity, 32, 147, 157, 176

substance abuse, treatment for, 67, 124–125, 130

suffering, 60, 61, 150

suicide, 125

surplus wealth, 79

taxation, 30–31, 98, 114, 125, 154, 155, 156, 167, 189

terminally ill patients, 65, 190. *See also* dying patients

'thin' theories of the good. *See*: human flourishing; human good(s)

trade-offs, 63, 135

tradition (and healthcare provision), 92, 94, 99, 102, 121, 167, 207n.2

treatment: benefits of, 60, 128, 129; burdensome, 60, 62, 119, 128, 129; extraordinary, 60; futile, 6, 87, 119; inappropriate, 167, 189; ineffective, 128; outcomes of, 61, 62; with ends other than healthcare, 6. *See also* medical treatment

truth: good of, 77; respect for, 42, 80–81, 131. *See also* lying

tubefeeding, 119, 122–123, 133; withdrawal of, 122, 140–141, 173–174, 190. *See also* starving patients

UK society, 100, 113, 116, 181

unconscious patients (irreversibly), 65, 119–123, 130, 133, 140–142, 190. *See also*: consciousness, level of; starving patients; tubefeeding

'universal destination' of world's resources, 155–156

universal healthcover, 46, 165, 166, 168, 189, 190

U.S.A., 16, 34, 39, 93, 100, 116, 173

utilitarian approaches to allocation, 16, 55–70, 185

utilitarianism, 55–70 *passim*, 203–204n.13. *See also*: Oregon Scheme; Quality Adjusted Life Years

utility maximization, 65–66, 68

valuing lives (economically), 60, 62

value neutrality of the state, 32, 35, 49–50, 96. *See also*: human good; human person, conceptions of

value of human life, 27, 148. *See also*: human life, respect for; sanctity of human life

vices (contrary to good healthcare), 81

virtue ethics, 74

virtues, moral, 75, 80–81, 97, 101, 103, 106, 158, 186; needed by doctors/nurses, 67, 80–81, 104–105, 161, 175, 186, 188; needed by patients, 80–81, 175. *See also* choice: and character

vocation (to healthcare), 103, 159, 188, 218–219n.11

vulnerable, concern for, 100

willingness to pay, 62

withdrawing/withholding care, 116, 140–141, 173–174. *See also*: British Medical Association; tubefeeding

withdrawing/withholding treatment, 43,
119, 138, 141. *See also* British
Medical Association
World Health Organization, 4, 167
'worthwhile life', 76. *See also*:

consciousness, level of; life: 'not
worth living'; quality of life

young patients, 65